FIRST AMERICAN
INTO SPACE

Navy Commander Alan Shepard, 37, father of two girls, 13-year-old Laura and 9-year-old Juliana, had no desire to be a hero.

What drove him to volunteer for the potentially dangerous task of probing the void beyond our planet?

Mostly, it was the chance to serve his country in a role for which he felt well qualified, but also because he saw it as a personal challenge.

No daredevil, he has a great, restless desire to do everything well, and then to do it a little better than the other fellow. As an astronaut, he could pit his strength against man and Nature with the added incentive of a thrilling ride beyond the Earth's atmosphere in a space capsule.

This unusual and timely book tells the whole story of Commander Shepard and his fantastic journey into outer space.

AUTHOR'S PROFILE

Robert Silverberg is a native of New York City and attended Columbia University. He became interested in space travel while still in elementary school, and has watched each new development in space science with keen interest since the days of V-2.

He began writing science fiction when he was in high school, and his first novel, REVOLT ON ALPHA C, was published by Thomas Y. Crowell while he was still in college. He has written some twenty science fiction novels under a variety of names, and has better than 600 published short stories and articles to his credit, many of them science fiction. In recent years he has written fiction and non-fiction in many fields.

He is married and lives in New York City. His wife is an electronics engineer engaged in government scientific research.

FIRST AMERICAN
INTO SPACE

★ ★ ★ ★ ★ ★ ★ ★ ★ ★ ★ ★ ★ ★ ★ ★ ★ ★ ★ ★

Robert Silverberg

MONARCH BOOKS, INC.

Derby, Connecticut

FIRST AMERICAN INTO SPACE

A Monarch Books Non-Fiction Special

Published in May, 1961

Copyright © 1961 by Monarch Books, Inc.

Monarch Books are published by MONARCH BOOKS, INC., Capital Building, Derby, Connecticut and represent the works of outstanding novelists and writers of non-fiction especially chosen for their literary merit and reading entertainment.

Printed in the United States of America

Chapter One

COMMANDER SHEPARD'S SPACE RIDE

It is 10:33 A.M., Eastern Daylight Saving Time, on Friday, May 5, 1961. At Cape Canaveral, Florida, a man sits alone in a small, cramped capsule atop a 69-foot-high Redstone rocket that is about to carry him on a journey through the airless dark of space.

He is Navy Commander Alan B. Shepard, Jr., 37 years old, born in New Hampshire in a year when radio was a novelty, television a dream, space travel a wild fantasy. He has been sealed into the Mercury capsule atop the rocket for more than four hours, waiting as patiently as he knows how for the moment when he will at last blast off for space.

Television cameras and the eyes of hundreds of onlookers focus intently on the shining spear that is the Redstone rocket standing alone on the launching pad now that the gantry crane has been rolled back. The countdown is in its final stages, ticking away with agonizing slowness, after three days of uncertainty. The rocket shot had been scheduled for the previous Tuesday, May 2, but menacing weather conditions then had prevented the attempt to send an American astronaut rocketing through space.

Even this morning, after Commander Shepard had been sealed into his capsule to await blast-off, a flurry of black clouds appearing suddenly in the sky over the Atlantic rocket range had threatened yet another postponement. But the clouds had soon drifted away.

And now the countdown is in its final moments, and an anxious world waits for the outcome. The United States is facing a challenge from its rival in the conquest of space, the Soviet Union. A few weeks earlier a Russian Cosmonaut, Yuri Gagarin, had staked for himself a place in history by becoming the first man to enter space. Gagarin, riding in a capsule not extremely different from the one Commander Shepard now waits in, had circled the Earth in orbit, spending some hundred-odd minutes in space before the firing of rockets had brought him back down to Earth.

The American exploit that is being attempted today is not quite as ambitious in scope. Yuri Gagarin, the Russians claim, attained a speed of nearly 18,000 miles an hour to go into orbit; the American astronaut will not reach a speed greater that 5,100 miles an hour. It has been reported that Gagarin had spent an hour and a half in space; our man would be up there only a handful of minutes. Gagarin had gone into orbit; our spaceman would only take a quick rocket ride.

Yet the shot would still be an important step for us. And the circumstances under which it is being made only add to the tension. No television cameras recorded Yuri Gagarin's flight; no radio commentators gave moment-by-moment eye-witness accounts. But here, at Cape Canaveral, with the ruthless eye of the camera pointed toward the launching pad, the pressures on everyone are enormous.

We cannot afford to fail. Even the most minor mishap will be immediately apparent, will stand out glaringly as an American failure in the face of Soviet success. And should the rocket blow up on the launching pad, should the astronaut's life be lost before an audience of millions, it would be the most publicized disaster in human history .

No one at the Cape lets himself think about the eventualities. The countdown goes on.

"T minus 30 seconds," comes the quiet voice.

The hands of the clock are moving. The countdown continues, without a stop now, without a hitch .

"Five. . . ."
"Four. . . ."
"Three. . . ."
"Two. . . ."
"One . . . mark!"
"Ignition!"
"Lift-off."

FIRST AMERICAN INTO SPACE

The moment has come! How many millions of breaths are drawn at that moment, no one will ever know. Nor will we ever really comprehend the thoughts in the mind of Alan Shepard as he feels the rumble of power beneath him.

A blaze of flame spurts from the tail of the Redstone rocket, now, and it rises into the air, hovering for a moment on its red tail of exhaust, then moving skyward, picking up speed as it ascends into the brilliantly blue sky. Rocket men, reporters, technicians, other astronauts let out a mighty whoop of jubilation.

The rocket knifes into the stratosphere now. A plume of white vapor appears as the rocket's skin comes into contact with the frigid air.

The time is exactly 10:34:13 A.M., Eastern Daylight Saving Time. America's first spaceman has left the launching pad. We are back in the space race once again!

Onward the capsule soars. The Redstone rocket drops away, leaving only the one-ton capsule moving through space with its fragile human cargo on board, the lonely man already many miles overhead, looking through his ports at the panorama of the Eastern United States spread out below him, cloud-flecked, beautiful.

The first words of the spaceman in the bell-shaped capsule reach Mercury Control Center at Cape Canaveral immediately after take-off. "OK. Full go," he says. Then he talks about the moments of blast-off, gives his reactions and later adds, "Cabin pressure OK." Then: "Fuel system go. Oxygen go. All systems go."

Finally there is a pause and the listening world hears: "Capsule in flight. Free of rocket. Switching to manual controls." And all the while Commander Shepard's voice is cool and controlled.

Then he says, "What a beautiful view." It is his first comment on what he sees. Up till now, he has been too busy simply reporting data on his flight, on the functioning of his capsule, on his own physical condition—everything up to par, everything going superbly. He adds quickly, "There is cloud cover to Cape Hatteras."

Commander Shepard goes on to give more details of his flight as the minutes pass. He has plenty to do. Unlike Yuri Gagarin, who apparently was simply a passenger during his space ride, the American astronaut has been trained to perform many tasks in his capsule. The purpose is to see how well a man functions in space, how capably he can carry out predetermined duties.

Now he fires the small jets that are designed to stabilize the capsule in its end-over-end flight. Everything still fine, he says. He tells the control center that the Redstone booster has been jettisoned right on schedule, leaving him free in his capsule. He is approaching the maximum speed of 5,100 miles an hour, and everything is functioning normally. The capsule is rising well along on the long arc that will take it through space and bring it down in the Atlantic Ocean some three hundred miles from its launching pad at Cape Canaveral.

At 10:37½, the astronaut describes how he is wiggling his control stick, demonstrating his unhampered ability to handle the capsule. In such a smooth flight, no piloting is required of him, but now it is known that he would have been able to deal with any emergency.

Two minutes later, he says he is firing the first of the three retro rockets behind him in the capsule's blunt nose. This is also only for testing purposes; the retro rockets play no part in his flight now, but when, later in the year, an American astronaut rides a similar capsule into orbit, the retro rockets will be needed to make possible the capsule's safe return to Earth.

"One has fired. Two has fired. Three has fired," he reports clearly, then adds, "Everything is going very smoothly."

Voice communication is coming through perfectly. The astronaut's transmissions are clear and sharp, and he is evidently in complete command of himself and the capsule. It is 10:41.

Now the retro rockets, having been tested and found functioning as expected, are jettisoned. They tumble away into the darkness. Casually, nervelessly, Cammander Shepard continues to report back a never-ceasing flow of data. He has been through this routine many, many times in drills held in simulated capsules on the ground. Now that the real thing is taking place, he speaks with practiced ease as he quietly calls off the readings from the bewildering maze of dials set into the instrument panel directly before him.

For five minutes, now, he has been weightless—devoid of all sensation of gravity. He reports in detail on what this is like. No American before him has known more than a few fleeting seconds of weightlessness, but now there are minutes of it. Shepard does not seem to find it a hardship.

$10:41\frac{1}{2}$, now.

The flight is seven minutes old, though it seems to the men at Cape Canaveral that many more minutes than that have gone by. The astronaut is beginning to descend. The outer skin of the capsule is starting to grow warm as the first fringes of the atmosphere are encountered.

Before the capsule touches down in the Atlantic, it may glow cherry-red with a heat of well over a thousand degrees, but the astronaut, insulated in his air-conditioned compartment within, will feel very little discomfort.

There is the first return of gravity now as the sense of weightlessness ends. Commander Shepard feels only one five-hundredth of normal gravitational pull, as the capsule skims back into the atmosphere. His weight seems to be only a few ounces. But, rapidly, the gravitational pull builds up as the capsule falls, blunt face foremost, through the thickening atmosphere. Although he is under fearful strain, his face distorted by the pull of gravity five and six and then nine, ten, eleven times that of normal ground-side conditions, he reports gamely everything that he is experiencing.

"Automatic controls performing properly," he calls. Then: "Nine G coming down. OK." There is a brief pause followed by: "Peak G Eleven. OK."

At 10:44, with the capsule well back into the atmosphere and the pull up to 11 G's, the small braking chute opens and he says, "First chute has deployed."

A minute later, with Commander Shepard's altitude at 10,000 feet, the main chute billows open, and the worst is over for Alan Shepard. The capsule, its wild fall arrested, dangles above the Atlantic, its descent from the peak height of 115 miles nearly terminated .

Recovery ships are getting into position in the Atlantic. The flight has been so successful that the pick-up crews are within a mile of the astronaut as the capsule comes down.

He reports again: everything going fine as the moment of impact approaches. The capsule, named Freedom VII by the seven astronauts who were originally selected to pilot it, is now clearly visible to the rescuers.

10:50½. The capsule hits the ocean at thirty feet a second.

Helicopters swarm like busy insects, hovering in the air as the capsule bobs into sight. They move in to complete the operation.

At 10:51, Copter 77, which is closest to the floating capsule, positions itself directly overhead, lowers a hook and a sling. The astronaut emerges, eases himself into the sling as the hook snares the capsule.

10:53. Capsule and astronaut are hoisted from the water by the copter, just nineteen minutes after the historic blast-off. At 11:02, they reach the deck of the Aircraft carrier *Lake Champlain*. The capsule comes to rest upright. Shepard descends from the capsule, planting his feet firmly on the deck of the aircraft carrier.

He is grinning, jaunty, seemingly undisturbed by the magnitude of his achievement.

"Boy, what a ride!" he exclaims. He sees his capsule on the carrier deck, frowns, walks toward it, ducks inside. He emerges a moment later, smiling broadly, holding the helmet of his space-suit. He had removed it when he hit the water, and had left it in the capsule.

Now, helmet under his arm, he moves forward to go below-decks for a preliminary physical checkup and debriefing session on his flight. Later that day, he lands at Grand Bahama Island for an intensive going-over, as doctors seek to discover what, if any, harmful effects are caused by such a trip through space.

He speaks to President Kennedy by radio telephone. After a weekend of medical checks, the astronaut will go to Washington for his formal welcome.

It is the tenth birthday of Shepard's younger daughter, Juliana. For Juliana—and for millions of others who waited anxiously through the taut, dramatic minutes of Commander Shepard's flight—the safe landing after the flawless space trip is the best of all possible gifts.

For Alan Shepard, the journey toward history began one day early in 1959, when he and several hundred other military test pilots were told of Project Mercury, America's program to send men on trips through space. Shepard volunteered, as did more than a hundred others, for the hazardous but heroic assignment. After months of rigorous testing, all but seven of the volunteers were eliminated. Shepard was one of the seven whose names were announced in April, 1959.

The Mercury program was to unfold in two phases. The first phase would see astronauts rocketed through space at 5,100 miles an hour over a 300-mile range, to test the reactions of the human body to the stresses of space travel. After that phase had been successfully completed, an astronaut would be sent up by a more powerful rocket at a speed of 18,000 miles an hour, and would go into orbit as a space satellite, circling the Earth three times, reporting back his observations, and then returning to our planet.

As time drew near for the first phase of Project Mercury, three men were chosen as finalists for the first sub-orbital or "ballistic" flight. These were Commander Shepard, Marine Lieutenant Colonel John Glenn, and Air Force Captain Virgil Grissom. The other four astronauts of the original group were held aside as reserves who would have their own turns at space flight later in the program.

During March and April of 1961, astronauts Glenn, Grissom, and Shepard drilled intensively for the space flight, with the understanding that the one considered in best condition at the time of the actual firing would be selected.

For a while, it seemed as though one of them would be the first human being ever to soar into space, but that honor was claimed by Yuri Gagarin on April 12. A few days later, Alan Shepard was notified that he had been chosen to make our first space flight. John Glenn was alerted to serve as stand-by in case Shepard came down with some last-minute ailment that might keep him from taking the space trip. Virgil Grissom remained on hand as Glenn's alternate.

On May 5, twenty-three days after the Gagarin flight, Alan Shepard rocketed aloft as America's first spaceman.

The tension had tightened around Shepard since Tuesday, May 2, the original target date for the firing. His name had been publicly announced; he had come almost to the point of going up, when the shot was cancelled. Shepard's wife and two daughters tried to go through a normal daily routine during the long hours that followed, while Shepard remained in seclusion rehearsing for the space shot.

Half an hour past midnight on May 5, the final countdown began for the second time. Shepard and his alternate, Glenn, had gone to bed at 10 P.M. for a few hours' sleep after a day of physical examinations during which they had been fed a special low-waste high-energy diet.

At 2:05 A.M., Shepard and Glenn were awakened on the orders of Dr. William Douglas, the head physician of the National Aeronautics and Space Agency. They showered, shaved, and breakfasted. Shepard's breakfast consisted of orange juice, two poached eggs, filet mignon wrapped in bacon, and dry toast. Breakfast over, Shepard and the astronaut Glenn went through yet another physical examination.

"As usual, they were in superb health," Dr. Douglas reported later in the day.

At 3:50 A.M. the astronauts were wired for telemetering observations. Electronic sensors were attached to their bodies at chest and throat. The sensors would later be connected to telemetering devices that would record the astronaut's heartbeat, respiration, and other physical responses during his flight. At 4:00 A.M., the two astronauts began the complicated half-hour job of climbing into their protective space-suits. Even with two assistants, it was a ticklish job to get into the heavy aluminized suits. When they were finished, Glenn and Shepard donned their helmets. Even though there was only the slimmest chance that John Glenn would make the flight in Shepard's place, he suited up anyway—just in case.

At 4:59, wearing suit and helmet, Commander Shepard glanced at Lieutenant Dee O'Hara, nurse to the astronauts.

"Here I go, Dee," he said, and he and Glenn made the eleven-step walk into the van that was waiting to take them to the launching pad. He carried his portable air-conditioning unit in his right hand, to keep him cool in the ponderous space suit until the capsule's cooling system took over.

At Launching Pad 5 at Cape Canaveral—the same pad from which America's first space satellite, Explorer I, had been launched in 1958—astronauts Glenn and Shepard, joined now by Grissom, gave the capsule a careful inspection. Expert engineers as well as test-pilots, they checked the capsule over thoroughly. At one point, Glenn discovered some moisture, and the countdown was held up while the matter was checked out. Finally, the pre-flight checks were over. Glenn and Grissom descended from the capsule; this was not to be their day of glory.

Alan Shepard was alone now.

At 7:10 A.M. the hatch was closed on the 9 by 6 capsule. Shepard settled down against his form-fitting contour couch. Pressure in his suit was five pounds per square inch. He was strapped in at shoulders, waist, and knees. All tests had been made, now. Blast-off time was set for 8 A.M. Minor adjustments delayed the shot for twenty-five minutes, and then the clouds appeared. Astronaut Shepard remained in his tiny capsule while the weather experts debated. The clouds began to break up; the countdown was resumed.

Now a new hitch developed. An inverter—a device that changes DC current to AC—was found to be faulty. More than an hour more went by while the repair was made. The spaceman waited patiently, maintaining radio contact with the technicians on the ground ten stories below and in the control center nearby. At last the count reached its final minutes.

At 10:34:13 the rocket was touched off. At once, the heavy fist of acceleration pushed Shepard against his contour couch. While anxious onlookers watched, the rocket climb out of sight, Shepard withstood a pull of gravity that more than quintupled his weight. Then, as the rocket booster burned out and dropped away, his weight fell to zero.

Onward he sped, out from Florida toward the landing point 300 miles away in the Atlantic, on an arc that took him 115 miles high. As he rode on, he continued a steady report to the control center, while manipulating controls that enabled him to cope with pitch, yaw, and roll. Then the capsule began to descend, and weight—crushing weight—piled on the astronaut again as he curved toward the Atlantic.

And then, finally, came the landing, the pick-up by the waiting helicopters, the trip to the carrier *Lake Champlain* and thence to the aluminum portable hospital erected especially at Grand Bahama Auxiliary Air Force Base for the medical check-up.

After a ride in the automobile of Captain Hugh May, Commander of the island missile tracking station, from the air field to the hospital, the astronaut was put to bed.

Colonel William Douglas, the astronauts' personal physician gave Commander Shepard a thorough physical examination and declared him to be in "excellent shape and health" and added that he doubted if he would show any ill effects from his awesome experience.

Later Commander Shepard was examined by Dr. George Ruff, a psychiatrist from the University of Pennsylvania and, again the report was excellent. In fact, Dr. Ruff stated he was both pleased and amazed that "Al was in such good shape."

The amazingly perfect flight was toasted in champagne at Grand Bahama Island with fellow astronaut, Captain Virgil Grissom, saying that Shepard "looks great, feels great. He is jolly and joking as Al always is."

Though Shepard was not permitted by the doctors attending him to drink any champagne, he later enjoyed eating a huge shrimp cocktail, a roast beef sandwich with iced tea for a beverage.

Congratulations poured in from every corner of the globe —although a sour Russian diplomat coldly observed that *his* country had accomplished such feats as Shepard's long ago. (This was in sharp contrast to President Kennedy's generous congratulations after Yuri Gagarin's flight.

Louise Shepard, the astronaut's wife, showed relief and pleasure at the safe conclusion of her husband's exploit. She had watched the flight on television from the very beginning.

Although she admitted that she was all "ducky bumps" at the moment of blast-off, she added with a wonderful winning smile, "I knew from the moment the rocket went up that Alan was going to be all right. I don't have to tell you how I feel. It's just wonderful. It's beautiful.

The wiry, 160-pound Shepard thus became the first of the seven Mercury Astronauts actually to take a flight through space. Son of a former Army man, he had a keen interest in science since his boyhood. In the 1941 yearbook of Admiral Farragut Academy, Toms River, N.J., which he attended before going on to the U.S. Naval Academy at Annapolis, it was written of him, "He speaks words of truth and soberness."

The shot was a triumph not only for Astronaut Shepard but for the entire team behind him—the six other astronauts who had helped in keeping the program moving and who had cheered Shepard on to his great accomplishment; Dr. Kurt Debus, the German rocket rocket scientist who had directed the final countdown; Wernher von Braun, the German space pioneer who had developed the Redstone rocket used as Shepard's booster into space; and literally hundreds of other scientists who had aided in preparation for the flight.

Two of the other astronauts had "chased" the Redstone rocket on its way up. The task fell to Scott Carpenter and Walter Schirra, who flew F106 fighter planes based at Patrick Air Force Base not far from Cape Canaveral. Carpenter flew at 25,000 feet, Schirra at 5,000, as the thousand-mile-an-hour jets made "eyeball" observations of the rocket's performance during the early stages of its flight.

A complex and skillfully engineered safety system had been set up in the event of any kind of failure. Atop the capsule as it blasted off, the fifteen-foot tower of an escape rocket jutted upward, ready to blow Shepard to safety in case the Redstone were to explode on launching. The escape rocket, not needed, was jettisoned after the safe blast-off.

In a press conference held the afternoon of Commander Shepard's feat, President Kennedy praised him for his accomplishment, saying, "We are awfully pleased and proud of what you did."

The President further stated that this marked a huge step forward in America's space program. But he added, sounding a sober note of warning, that we still had a long way to go before we matched the Russian space achievements, and called on the nation to "redouble" its space effort.

The conversation, via radio telephone, between President Kennedy and Commander Shepard was informal and full of cheer and the high spirits felt by everyone in America: THE PRESIDENT: "I want to congratulate you very much."

COMMANDER SHEPARD: "Thank you very much, Mr. President."

THE PRESIDENT: "We watched you on TV, of course, and we are awfully pleased and proud of what you did."

COMMANDER SHEPARD: "Well, thank you, sir. As you know by now, everything worked out just about perfectly. And it was a very rewarding experience for me and for the people who made it possible."

THE PRESIDENT: "We are looking forward to seeing you up here, Commander."

COMMANDER SHEPARD: "Thank you very much. I am looking forward to it, I assure you."

THE PRESIDENT: "The members of the National Security Council are meeting on another matter this morning, and they all want me to give you their congratulations."

COMMANDER SHEPARD: "Thank you very much, sir, and I am looking forward to meeting you."

Already, $400,000,000 had gone into Project Mercury during the two-and-a-half years of its existence, and the project is not yet completed. The cost thus far has been $2.25 for every man, woman, and child in the United States. As the space program continues, expenditures will mount. Now that Alan Shepard's pioneering flight has cleared the way, other ballistic flights will follow, utilizing the services of the other six astronauts. And then, late in 1961 or perhaps early in 1962, an American spaceman will be placed in orbit.

Which spaceman will it be? At this stage, nobody knows. During the months to come, further tests will demonstrate the capabilities of each of the seven Mercury Astronauts. Perhaps the man chosen to make the first American orbital flight will be Commander Alan Shepard—or perhaps that spaceman's name will be Glenn, Grissom, Schirra, Slayton, Cooper, or Carpenter. It depends on a whole spectrum of factors that will alter constantly between now and the time the countdown begins for that orbital shot.

Until that day, Commander Alan Shepard's May 5 flight must stand as the peak of American space accomplishment. It is an historic achievement, due to take its place in the annals of man's conquest of the unknown universe.

Chapter Two

THE SPACE RACE

On the morning of July 30, 1955, it seemed that all of America's newspapers had turned abruptly into science fiction publications. U.S. TO BUILD TINY MOON TO CIRCLE EARTH, screamed the staid New York *Herald Tribune* across eight columns that Saturday morning. And, in only slightly smaller type, it went on to declare: RUSSIA JOINS IN RACE, PLANS A SIMILAR SATELLITE. Stunningly, science fiction was to be transformed into science fact.

James C. Hagerty, President Eisenhower's press secretary, called reporters together to inform them of the epochal announcement. And so our space program was born, somewhat of a stepchild—since little attention was paid to it after its birth—which brought us, twenty-six months later, one of the worst humiliations in our history.

Almost unnoticed in the publicity barrage over our satellite program was the quiet statement of an unnamed government scientist, released the same day. "It is quite possible the Soviet Union may be preparing to launch an Earth satellite similar to the one announced by the United States," he was quoted in a UP dispatch. He went on to say that Russia "may be as far along in satellite research as the United States, and perhaps even farther along."

His statement was ignored. After all, American science was supreme, wasn't it? We had given the world the airplane, radio, television, the telephone, the phonograph, the automobile—why, virtually every important technological advance of the past three generations. What had the Russians accomplished, besides making a lot of fantastic claims to have invented everything first? We laughed the story into oblivion.

Complacence—apathy—overconfidence. Those were the American sins of 1955-1957. We paid for them in the rueful awakening of October 4, 1957, Sputnik Day, when the myth of American space supremacy was shattered. After that day, we could no longer go on assuming automatically that we would lead the way in scientific advances. Suddenly, we found it necessary to take a new, hard look at ourselves.

Just as the attack on Pearl Harbor ripped us out of our cocoon of isolationism and spearheaded our war effort as no other event might have done, so did the Soviet space triumph of 1957 spur us out of our mid-Fifties slumbers, and goad us to the succession of space triumphs that has been climaxed now with the entry of an American into space.

To understand the meaning of Project Mercury, we have to go back, to explore the background, and see how the tenacious dream of a few pioneers has been turned into reality.

Reaching the stars is mankind's oldest dream. The heavens are the abode of the gods—and since earliest days man has longed to bound skyward, to snatch for himself the mantle of godhood. Written space fiction goes back at least two thousand years, to Lucian of Samosata, who told of a crew of adventurers carried by a waterspout to the Moon.

For twenty centuries, such tales remained in the realm of fantasy. But a dedicated few worked at the task of giving reality to man's Moonward quest. One was a Russian theoretician, Konstantin Eduardovich Tsiolkovski, whose speculations on space flight began to appear in Russian journals as far back as 1895. By 1903, he had published a paper on a liquid-fueled rocket ship. In 1913, he wrote prophetically, *"Mankind will not stay on the Earth forever, but, in the pursuit of the world and space, will at first timidly penetrate beyond the limits of the atmosphere and then will conquer all the space around the sun."*

Tsiolkovski's theoretical work laid the groundwork for rocket science. He was hailed as a national hero on his 75th birthday, in 1932. His disciples were active in Russian rocket research all through the Thirties, but the fruits of their labors were first turned not toward building spaceships but toward designing rockets to hurl back the German invaders of 1941.

Another great name in rocket science is that of an American, Dr. Robert Hutchings Goddard. He brought the rocket out of the theoretical tomes and onto the testing grounds. From 1914 on, he built and fired an amazing series of rockets, despite public scorn and harassment. On March 16, 1926, a Goddard-built rocket powered by gasoline and liquid oxygen climbed 41 feet in two and a half seconds. In that sputtering, halting flight, the first step to the stars was taken.

Goddard worked on, perfecting his rockets, until by 1935 he had succeeded in firing one that climbed 4800 feet straight up, then traveled horizontally for 2½ miles at a speed of 550 miles an hour It was an incredible performance.

When the war came, Goddard designed fuel pumps for take-off boosters. He died almost in obscurity, four days before V-J Day, having lived to see his pioneering work adapted by his country's enemies into engines of war.

For not only Goddard and Tsiolkovski had worked on the space frontier. The third great name of rocket science is that of a German, Dr. Herman Oberth, who published— without knowledge of Tsiolkovski's work—his own book of rocket theory, and who went on, all during th: Thirties, to carry out rocket experiments in Germany on a grand scale. By 1937, German rocket scientists, led by the brilliant young Wernher von Braun, had produced the A-4, a monster rocket 46 feet high that could carry a one-ton warhead almost two hundred miles. This was no rickety toy. It was a full-fledged ballistic missle, a direct ancestor of today's Titan and Atlas.

Von Braun's team at the Peenemunde testing base worked day and night on their A-4, only to run into that ubiquitous bugaboo of rocket research, governmental thriftiness. Flushed with the confidence of his early victories, Hitler saw the missile program as a needless extravagance, and cut it to the bone in 1940. Not till eighteen months later, when the tide of war had begun to turn against the Nazis, did Hitler recollect his rocket scientists at Peenemunde. By that time, Soviet rockets were wreaking havoc on the Eastern front. Von Braun's group was hastily reactivated, and the A-4's budget restored.

The first two test firings were failures. But on the third try, in the spring of 1942, the giant rocket thundered into the sky, hurtled far into the stratosphere at a mind-numbing 3500 miles per hour, and landed as planned in the Baltic Sea, 120 miles away.

"Do you realize what we accomplished today?" exclaimed Nazi General Walter Dornberger, watching the shot. *"Today the spaceship was born!"*

But the needs of war took priority over the conquest of the planets. The A-4, rechristened the V-2, went into immediate production as a war weapon. The project suffered a severe setback in August, 1943, when RAF bombers attacked Peenemunde and damaged the base heavily, killing hundreds of technicians and engineers. The project went underground and, despite Allied attacks, was turning out 20 V-2s a month by the fall of 1943, stepping up production to 300 a month the following spring, and then to 900 a month.

In the summer of 1944, after D-Day, major field tests of the V-2 took place. Though, at first, two thirds of the missiles broke apart upon launching, the bugs were speedily removed. On September 6, 1944, the era of missile warfare began: the first V-2s were fired at England.

Had Nazi rocket research proceeded without interruption during 1940 and 1941, the outcome of the war might have been significantly different. But by the end of 1944, the thousand-year Reich was visibly crumbling, and not even the terrifying new weapon could save Hitler's regime. Russian troops pounded mercilessly toward the German rocket installations at Peenemunde. A secret plan was conceived to execute 500 of the top missile scientists and technicians in case their capture by the Allies became likely—but this plan was never put into effect.

The Russians occupied Peenemunde and captured many of these German engineers and technicians, but the top men, those who had been in charge of long-range planning, escaped with Dornberger and von Braun and gave themselves up to the Americans.

There is considerable room for argument about which

side got more of the scientists—the Russians at one point claimed the edge—but there is no doubt that we got the real experts, the cream of the crop. Nor is there any doubt that both sides benefited by, and built on, the German experience with rocketry—to what extent no one can accurately figure.

We do know that our windfall was fabulous. We captured more than a hundred V-2s intact. Our "Operation Paperclip" rounded up 150 top-flight German rocket scientists, and offered them 5-year research contracts in the United States, at attractive terms. We acquired V-2 blueprints, parts, test equipment.

In one fell swoop at the end of World War II the United States made itself the possessor of the world's most advanced space technology. The universe was ours for the taking. Yet for twelve years thereafter, we moved forward at a snail-like crawl, sublimely confident that space would wait for us.

Space waited. But the eager comrades did not. With an effort that even the bitterest anti-Communist must admit was truly magnificent, the Russians sped past us and won the first heat of the space race before we even realized a race was going on.

Our postwar rocket research was far from negligible. The average voter and the average government official took a couldn't-care-less attitude toward space exploration, but every great adventure of mankind from Columbus onward has faced the same difficulty. A few far-sighted men continued to wring a minuscule cash supply out of Congress each year for our space program.

An American rocket program had been under way since 1944. We had already developed a solid-fuel, high-altitude rocket known as the "Private," and in 1945 it was succeeded by a slender, 16-foot-long vehicle known as the WAC-Corporal, America's first major rocket, which soon attained heights of 40 miles. Two years later, we added the Aerobee to our growing rocket family—eighteen feet in length, and capable of carrying a 154-pound payload to a height of 70 miles. We used Aerobee and WAC-Corporal rockets to explore the upper atmosphere and the lower reaches of space, sometimes attaching them to a captured V-2 for greater boost.

Thus, in February, 1949, a WAC-Corporal, boosted by a German-made V-2, raced a breath-taking 252 miles above Earth's surface—man's first genuine stab into the darkness of space. The shot, at our White Sands, New Mexico proving grounds, was history-making for another reason: it was the first large-scale, two-stage rocket. The V-2 had carried 20 miles spaceward at nearly 4,000 feet per second. At a pre-timed moment, the two rockets separated, the heavy V-2 dropped back to Earth, and the slim WAC-Corporal began to spout flame and spurt upward on its own power. The delicate feat of firing a rocket in flight and detaching the booster had been carried off successfully.

But that 1949 flight marked a peak in American rocketry that seemed hard to surpass. Succeeding two-stage flights, that spring, misfired. Others were successful, but failed to top the February performance. Still, a major step forward had been taken. A combination of German and American skills had put man on the threshold of space.

While our rockets gradually evolved, other plans were in the discussion stage. In 1950, an international meeting of scientists announced that seven years hence a world-wide investigation of our planet would be undertaken, an eighteen-month program to be known as the International Geophysical Year.

During the eighteen months of the I.G.Y., scientists of every country would co-operate in a gigantic program of research aimed at unveiling our planet's secrets. From the start, it was considered desirable to launch a number of rocket probes to explore the outer atmosphere and the fringes of space itself. But, by October 4, 1954, the planners of the I.G.Y. resolved to make an even bolder suggestion:

"In view of the great importance of observations over extended periods of time of extraterrestrial radiations and geophysical phenomena in the upper atmosphere, and in view of the advanced state of present rocket techniques, it is recommended that thought be given to the launching of small satellite vehicles, to their scientific instrumentation, and to the new problems associated with satellite experiments, such as power supply, telemetering, and orientation of the vehicle."

The idea of putting a space satellite in orbit—of creating an artificial moon—was not precisely new. The mathematics of it had been known for decades, and elaborate plans for space stations had been features of science fiction stories as far back as 1929. What needed to be done was to launch the satellite at such a speed that its centrifugal force would keep it either from falling back to Earth or from flying off into space. If the right speed were attained at the right distance from Earth, the satellite would remain fixed in orbit, indefinitely circling the planet, subject only to friction with Earth's atmosphere or collision with wandering space particles.

As far back as 1948, the U.S. Government had been seriously considering a space satellite program. Secretary of Defense James Forrestal had announced, on December 29, 1948, that we were studying the possibility of building a huge satellite station 22,300 miles out in space, to be used as a site from which we could threaten our enemies with space bombardment.

But there was more fantasy than fact in this 1948 announcement. Such a station is beyond our capabilities to construct even today; in 1948, the idea was pure Buck Rogers. Still, Forrestal's suggestion did indicate that the government had a certain degree of receptivity to such way-out notions. It may have helped to smooth the way, six years later, for acceptance of the I.G.Y. committee's seemingly fantastic plans for scientific satellites.

The I.G.Y. sponsors could not launch satellites themselves; even the smallest satellite program would need millions of dollars. Through the National Science Foundation, a government agency created to encourage scientific progress, the I.G.Y. scientists lobbied energetically for Congressional and Pentagon support. By early 1955, they had acquired a powerful ally: the late Donald A. Quarles, then Assistant Secretary of Defense for Research and Development.

Unknown to the I.G.Y. people, a military satellite program was already under way, known as Project Orbiter. Several influential missile scientists, led by Wernher von Braun, had persuaded the Pentagon of the feasibility of a satellite program. In the summer of 1954, von Braun told Army and Navy representatives that he could put a satellite in orbit within two years or less, *using existing equipment*. In the five years since the WAC-Corporal's flight, we had developed a number of powerful ballistic missiles, and von Braun proposed using the big Redstone missile, a liquid-fuel rocket with 75,000 pounds of thrust, with Loki missiles—smaller, and solid-fueled—forming the second and third stages. He guaranteed to put a 15-pound satellite into orbit using this off-the-shelf hardware.

If is a tormenting word. If von Braun had had his way, we might have had a space satellite in orbit a full year before Sputnik.

In 1954, it seemed that von Braun would have his satellite. The Office of Naval Research established Project Orbiter, preliminary contracts were approved and—in January, 1955—the entire project went to the Defense Department to be brought to President Eisenhower's attention, in line with the chain-of-command structure of his administration. But the story of the project got pigeonholed somewhere in the Pentagon. The President never found out about it.

While the Army and Navy were jointly pushing Project Orbiter, the Air Force was working out an even more startling plan—Project Moon. The intention was to send a 150-pound payload to the Moon via a four-stage rocket. But Pentagon wrangles killed this project before it reached final stages.

Project Orbiter moved along through the spring of 1955, toward the goal of an American space satellite for military purposes. At the same time the I.G.Y. scientists continued to press for a research satellite.

The left hand seemed not to know what the right hand was doing. Project Orbiter had been budgeted out of regular funds, and there was no need to get formal Presidential approval. Whether out of neglect or out of a deliberate failure of communication, no one bothered to let the President know. So, although Project Orbiter had been conceived during his Administration, President Eisenhower, by his own admission, was unaware of both the Orbiter program and of the I.G.Y. suggestion until the late spring of 1955, when the I.G.Y. scientists succeeded in putting their proposition to him. Two years later, the President said, "The first mention that was made of an intercontinental— of an earth satellite that I know of, was about the spring of 1955—I mean the first mention to me—following upon a conference in Rome where plans were being laid for the working out of things to be done in the International Geophysical Year."

The President approved the I.G.Y. group's request, and on July 29, 1955, the Hagerty press conference broke the news: there was to be a satellite program conducted for the sake of science. It was to have no military aspect whatever, and the scientific data to be gathered would be shared with all nations—including the Soviet Union.

The announcement caused a considerable stir, but no one was more astonished by it than the Project Orbiter team. They knew nothing of the new Project Vanguard. The President knew nothing of them. In a moment's time, their project was down the drain after a year's work. The Navy was given exclusive control over the I.G.Y. satellite. Instead of using off-the-shelf missiles as von Braun had proposed, an entirely new rocket would be designed, based on the exciting Viking rocket that had been under development since 1948.

It would take thousands of words to untangle and examine the webwork of decisions that led to the scrapping of Project Orbiter, the relegation of von Braun and his team to the sidelines, and the granting of a monopoly of satellite work to Project Vanguard. In looking back, we can see the enormity of the error committed by our government in 1955.

But the arguments of the other side had a certain hollow validity at the time. It was felt that it was best to emphasize the peaceful nature of Project Vanguard by entrusting the work to a group that was not already identified with the building of missiles for war. And the Navy insisted that

Vanguard would be less costly than any other satellite program. All they were asking was a mere $10,000,000, with a supplementary reserve of $12,000,000 more.

The reaction to our Vanguard announcement was varied. Some Congressmen grumbled that it was ridiculous to spend as much as a dime on space exploration. On the other hand, Representative Melvin Price of Illinois, a member of the Atomic Energy Committee, declared that $10,000,000 "wouldn't begin to finance" an adequate program of man-made satellites. The general public was apathetic. 1955 was the auto industry's greatest year, and public interest in tailfins and chrome was far greater than in shooting basketballs into outer space.

Another who shared the general hostility toward the project was Secretary of Defense Charles E. Wilson. It was he who had scornfully declared, "Pure research is what you do when you don't know what you're doing." It was Wilson who had said, at a press conference in November 1954, replying to a suggestion that the Russians might forge ahead of us in missile technology and put a satellite into space, "I wouldn't care if they did." Even after the Sputnik launching, Wilson shrugged if off as nothing but a "trick."

Perhaps he cannot be blamed for failing to grasp the magnitude of the adventure into space, and he was far from alone. Even today, many of the strongest advocates of space research seem to share Wilson's conviction that space exploration for its own sake is a frivolous extravagance, but that we should explore the universe "for military reasons" or "because if we don't the Russians will."

It should not be thought that bungling of our space program was a Republican monopoly. Certainly the Eisenhower Administration acted neither wisely nor well in furthering space research, at least not until it was goaded to a greater effort by the Russian triumphs. But the Democratic Truman Administration that preceded it showed no particular grasp of the importance of space research, either. Although we had sense enough to acquire German scientists and their V-2 rockets, and though we did attempt to move on from there, our efforts were hampered by interservice rivalries and by noncomprehension on the highest levels, and we rapidly frittered away our original lead.

FIRST AMERICAN INTO SPACE

Those men farsighted enough to understand the urgency of needed action in the '40s and early '50s were turned into Cassandras, into prophets without honor. Frustrated and thwarted, many of them left government or military service, and now have important roles in the corporations belatedly receiving our space contracts. Thus, the initial impetus for the Atlas missile dates from 1951—but not until 1953 was anything tangible done to implement the original decision to build the I.C.B.M.

Under President Eisenhower, the space budget was increased, the first plans for satellite shots were approved, and the concept of the missile became generally accepted. These are decisions to the Administration's credit. But what was actually accomplished turned out to be too little, too late.

At any rate, we did have a space satellite program going —of sorts—as of July 29, 1955. A month later, rocket scientists attending the Sixth International Astronautical Congress in Copenhagen were addressed by a Russian space scientist, Dr. Leonid Sedov. He announced boastfully that no later than 1957, a Soviet space satellite would be in orbit around Earth. It would be heavier than anything the United States would be capable of launching. And, in all probability, it would be placed in orbit ahead of any American satellites.

After ten years of the cold war, we were accustomed to discounting all Russian boasts of this sort as mere propagandistic drum-beating. Sedov's words were laughed away. Project Vanguard was under way, and who could doubt that it would be an American satellite that would first buzz round the Earth?

But Project Vanguard was born a stepchild. From the very first, it was a low-priority, low-budget operation. Dr. Clifford C. Furnas, a Defense Department official until resigning in disgust early in February 1957, declared that the Vanguard project had been crippled by "begrudging and dribbling financial support." Funds for expansion of the project were consistently refused. "There has been," Furnas said, "a great deal of fumbling, waiting for the other fellow to pick up the check."

27

Underbudgeted, undernourished, the Vanguard soon became a bitter joke in engineering circles. The prime contractor on the project, the Martin Company, worked valiantly within the limits of the skimpy budget allowed it. But corners had to be cut. Safety margins were shaved again and again. The Vanguard was turning out to be a minimum rocket, one that was just barely capable of performing its tasks if everything functioned perfectly.

The American public knew nothing of this. Press releases streamed regularly from Washington, and we drowsed with the comfortable delusion that "something" was being done about space research.

Something. But not very much.

The initial Vanguard budget of $22,000,000 proved to be ridiculously inadequate. The program directors scrounged for more funds, but ran up against what Dr. Furnas called "the chronic monetary constipation of the armed forces." Dollars trickled out of the exchequer at a maddeningly slow rate.

We heard little from the Russians during these months of 1956 and 1957. They had made their boasts, and we had smiled, and that was that.

The Vanguard satellite carrier took form. It stood 72 feet high, 45 inches in diameter at its thickest—a glistening needle weighing 11 tons. Its first stage consisted of fuel tanks, a motor and an apparatus section. Stage Two, adapted from the Aerobee-Hi rocket, had a delicate control section far more sophisticated than anything else ever built in this country or in Germany. Stage Three was a solid-fuel rocket that carried the satellite on its nose.

Pound for pound, our Vanguard was a superb little rocket. It weighed three tons less than the V-2, and delivered five times as much velocity. It was capable of fantastic precision performance. It *had* to be—because the budgeteers hadn't left room for safety margins.

The first Vanguard test was held on December 8, 1956, at Cape Canaveral, Florida. The slim rocket shot upward in a blinding blaze, streaking over the Atlantic at 4,000 miles an hours. Automatic timing switches functioned perfectly. The first test was considered a total success. A second test, on May 1, 1957, was also encouraging.

28

FIRST AMERICAN INTO SPACE

But there was much work yet to be done before the rocket would be able to blast into space, attain a velocity of 18,000 miles an hour, and put its basketball-sized cargo into the desired orbit. All during the spring and summer of 1957, our rocket men modified and tested and modified again, bringing the Vanguard ever closer to operational status.

We were acting as though no such thing as a space race existed. Even when malcontents would point out the possibility of a Russian first in space, we shrugged the idea away. This was scientific research, not a child's game. What did it matter which nation reached space first? Soon enough, we would both be there. We took a lofty and noncompetitive attitude toward the entire project—failing completely to foresee the dramatic consequences of the Russian triumph.

Virtually to the end of 1957, the Defense Department continued to dole out Vanguard funds in a niggardly way. Dr. Furnas, in his blistering attack on the go-slow policy, said that the official attitude was "since the satellite is not to be a piece of military weapon hardware, it is only a 'scientific toy' and hence not worthy of high priority attention or major support."

The Vanguard engineering team continued to toil. The deadline for the first satellite shot was moved back—from the summer of 1957 to the fall, from the fall of 1957 to the spring of 1958. Sooner or later, Project Vanguard would be a reality, we were told.

The rude awakening came on October 4, 1957.

At 5:58 P.M., EDT, the myth of American superiority was punctured by a ringing announcement from the official Soviet news agency, Tass:

"As a result of the intensive work by research institutes and designing bureaus the first artificial earth satellite in the world has now been created. The first satellite was successfully launched in the U.S.S.R. on October 4."

It was not just another Russian hoax. It was up there, whizzing around the world at five miles a second, giving off a *beep-beep* sound that became all too familiar in the days that followed. The *beep-beep* of the Soviet satellite served as the alarm signal to wake us from our slumbers.

Sputnik, it was called. "Fellow-traveler," a punning name that only served to rub in our humiliation a little deeper. It circled the world every 96 minutes. Scientist Leonid Sedov, whose 1955 words had gone unheard, scoffed, "You Americans have a better standard of living than we have. But the American loves his car, his refrigerator, his house. He does not, as the Russians do, love his country." Sedov went on, with monstrous sarcasm, to offer space in a forthcoming Russian satellite for a few American scientific instruments—hitchhikers into the void.

Not since the Pearl Harbor fiasco had our national pride been so deeply stung. The chorus of praise for Russian science, from Thailand to London, implicitly mocked us for our complacency and cockiness.

A major self-examination of America's goals, values, and beliefs began the next morning. Many intellectual leaders actually welcomed the Sputnik, for its importance as a stimulus to re-evaluate our entire way of life. Adlai Stevenson called it "that blessed, brazen angel which at last disturbed our slothful slumber."

One thing was certain. We could no longer afford to drag our feet in space research. Space travel was no longer a dream of fantasy writers. Rocket research was no longer the province of amateur experimenters. We had to face the prospect of being left behind while the Communists staked their claim to the universe.

And so our chagrined planners sat down to work out a revised program for space, a crash program embracing space satellites of diverse kinds, re-entry operations, and—the project that has now reached culmination—the sending of a human being into space, and his return.

October 4, 1957 marked a turning point in our attitude toward space. On that day, the space race began in earnest.

Chapter Three

FROM SPUTNIK TO PROJECT MERCURY

The impact of that first Soviet Sputnik was immediate and enormous. As late as August, 1957, we had shrugged off Premier Khrushchev's claim of an operational U.S.S.R. ballistic missile as propaganda—but now the proof of Russian rocket supremacy was indisputable. Even those scientists who had gloomily been aware of Red missile progress and who had been fully expecting the satellite coup were astonished at the size of Sputnik I. Dr. Joseph Kaplan, chairman of the U.S. program for the International Geophysical Year, described the 184-pound weight as "fantastic." This country had been hopefully planning to launch a satellite of a mere twenty-one and a half pounds—and even that launching looked problematical.

President Eisenhower, in congratulating the Russian scientists' achievement, promised that we would cease to drag our own heels. New budget appropriations were rushed through. Educators urged high school students to plan for engineering careers. Overnight, the scientist was elevated from the crackpot class to the role of potential national savior.

Of course, there were still the scoffers in high places. Rear Admiral Rawson Bennett, Chief of Naval Operations, referred to Sputnik I as a "hunk of iron almost anybody could launch." He grudgingly admitted that the Russian satellite was probably in orbit, but was skeptical about the claimed weight of 184 pounds.

Admiral Bennett and others like him soon had reason to swallow their skepticism. While our weary Vanguard engineers worked round the clock to satisfy mounting national pressures for an American space shot, the now jubilant

Russians hurled a *second* Sputnik into space, only a month after the first. And this one was not only a monster that dwarfed the "fantastic" size of Sputnik I, it carried a passenger to boot!

Sputnik II took to orbit on November 3, 1957. Its weight was a staggering 1120 pounds. It carried instruments for studying solar radiation, cosmic rays, and two radio transmitters for reporting data to Earth. Also aboard, the Russians said, was a dog in an air-conditioned container— the now-famous space dog "Laika."

The enormous weight of Sputnik II—and the fact that the Russians had succeeded in putting a living creature into orbit—increased American fears and chagrin. It was obvious now, that they had rockets whose lifting power far exceeded anything we would have for years to come. And, American experts quietly pointed out, if the Russians could hurl half a ton of satellite into an orbit 900 miles above Earth's surface, they could certainly send a much lighter H-bomb to any chosen area of this country at will.

Grimly now, we set about to recoup some of our lost scientific prestige. A Vanguard test shot had already been scheduled for the first week of December. Previous tests had been held secretly. Now the full glare of publicity was turned on the operation. Both the first and third stages of the Vanguard rocket had been tested successfully, but never the complex second stage. Martin Company officials, well aware of the hazards of rocket tests, had openly expressed doubt that a perfect shot could be attained on the first attempt.

But we went ahead. In place of the 20-inch satellite, a 6½-inch dummy globe was used. We stressed the fact that this was only a preliminary test. But in the eyes of the world, this was the first American satellite shot. The fact that one component of the vehicle was getting its first test went unnoticed.

On December 4, the countdown began, but so many mechanical difficulties occurred that the shot had to be postponed for two days. The shot finally took place on December 6—and ended in crushing fiasco. Oddly, it was not the untried second stage but the hitherto reliable first stage that failed. At the moment of launching, the first stage malfunctioned. The rocket fell back on the launching pad and was destroyed in flame. To the insult of the two Sputink launchings was added the injury of the highly public failure of our own first satellite try.

At this point Wernher von Braun's Project Orbiter was abruptly reactivated. Von Braun's plans for an Army-sponsored satellite had been gathering dust since interde-partmental rivalry had scuttled them in 1955, but now a transfusion of dollars brought Orbiter back to life. The new Secretary of Defense, Neil McElroy, instructed von Braun's Army team to go into action independent of the Navy's Vanguard crew, in the hope that someone would succeed in launching an American satellite.

Von Braun produced. He made use of the powerful Jupiter-C missile—a descendant of the Redstone rocket proposed originally by Project Orbiter—and on January 31, 1958, only six week after revival of the Army project, Americans heaved a collective sigh of relief as the first American space satellite roared into orbit. The eighty-inch-long Explorer I weighed only eighteen pounds, but at least it was up there. The plan that had been sidetracked in 1955 had yielded us our first space triumph in 1958.

It was no longer time for recriminations and hindsight. We had proved we could do it; now the task was to settle down and do it better, and do it more often. The President appointed a board of advisers to co-ordinate our space pro-gram. A far-ranging series of projects was scheduled.

Less than a week after the Explorer launching, the hapless Vanguard team tried again. But the rocket broke apart in midair within sixty seconds. Another shot, on March 17, 1958, brought belated but gratifying success, as a 6-inch "grapefruit" satellite achieved orbit. And—after a disheart-ening series of further failures—a full-sized 20-inch Van-guard satellite, weighing 10 pounds, went into orbit on February 17, 1959. The third and last of the Vanguard satellites took its place in the skies the following September, after which the program was concluded.

Ironically, Project Vanguard, which scored three successes in a dozen tries, might under other circumstances have been hailed as a great national triumph. But, thanks to the re-lentless publicity that accompanied its quite expectable failures, it has been and will be considered a botched operation—unjustly.

During 1958 the United States consolidated its space position. The national hysteria over our 1957 humiliation abated as satellite after satellite hurled into orbit, until a new success became not even a front-page event. Von Braun's group orbited a second Explorer in March, a third one in July. In December, an entire Atlas missile was placed into orbit—a "satellite" of eight thousand pounds' weight—and President Eisenhower's Christmas greetings were beamed to the world via electronic relay. By the end of 1958, we had orbited no less than five satellites.

The Russians, after their two sensational accomplishments of 1957, spent 1958 in apparent retrenchment. Aside from the launching of Sputnik III in May, a massive ton-and-a-half satellite, we heard of no other Soviet space accomplishments during that entire year. We began to realize that we were not hopelessly out of the space picture. Some advantages lay on both sides.

The great Russian advantage, we saw now, was the powerful thrust of its launching rocket. Apparently, some time in the mid-1950s, the Soviets had scored a breakthrough in rocket power which permitted them to lift great tonnages. Our rockets did not, and do not today, have the thrust of the Soviet vehicles. What we do have, however, is sophistication of technology. Our space rockets are more precise, more elegantly designed. We have a broad base of electronics research that has produced a spectacular array of control and telemetering devices. Our superior technology enables us to put up more different kinds of satellites—but, as of now, we lack the raw force of the Russian rockets.

As an engineer working on our satellite program put it in recent conversation, "Comparing our space operation with the Russian operation is like comparing a boxer with a puncher. The boxer, he'll finesse you to death with stylish footwork and light taps, and he'll win a lot of fights. The puncher just comes out swinging for all he's worth. He's not graceful, but if he ever connects—man, you're dead!"

And so the Russian space drive has taken the form of ponderous, widely spaced shots of heavy equipment, while we have thrown up a profusion of smaller, more artfully packaged satellites—through the spring of 1961, a total of nearly *forty,* as against a mere dozen for the Soviet Union. In both programs, the essential goals are the same—to develop a fund of scientific information through satellite findings, to probe the Moon and nearer planets, to explore the vicinity of the Sun, and ultimately to send men into space. We can best understand the startling diversity of our space efforts of the last three years by making a category-by-category breakdown of what has been done.

Satellites of Earth

The Russians got there first. To date, we're far ahead in over-all quantity of satellites orbited, but the Russian Sputniks have been bigger.

Moon Probes

Here we have been in difficulties, thanks to superior Russian rocket thrust. A Russian lunar probe called *Mechta* (Daydream) and also known as *Lunik I* was launched on January 2, 1959. It missed the Moon by less than five thousand miles, continuing onward to go into an orbit around the Sun. On September 12, 1959, *Mechta II* was more successful, a history-making shot that actually landed an 860-pound capsule on the Moon a day and a half after launching. To date this is the only successful Moon shot. *Mechta III,* launched October 4, 1959 to commemorate the second anniversary of the first Sputnik firing, added to man's knowledge by circling the Moon and taking the first photographs of the Moon's hitherto unseen far side. The Russians quickly—and legitimately—named the new features thus discovered, and so the Moon now has such landmarks as the Sea of Moscow and the Tsiolkovski Crater.

Our own Moon shots have been far less successful, to put it mildly. We made our first attempt on October 11, 1958, with the Pioneer I. It set a short-lived altitude record of 71,300 miles, but fell back 160,000 miles short of the Moon itself. Pioneer II dropped back to Earth after a flight of only a thousand miles, in November, 1958. Pioneer III, a month later, reached 66,000 miles, again a failure, but yielded important scientific results when it discovered the Van Allen radiation belt around the Earth.

Our fourth Pioneer probe, on March 4, 1959, succeeded in escaping from Earth's gravitational pull, unlike its three predecessors, but it missed the Moon by 37,300 miles and went into orbit around the Sun. It, too, has radioed back important scientific data about sunspots and solar radiation.

Our Moon probes, then, have been scientifically valuable in gathering information on conditions in space. The Russians, though, have scored two impressive triumphs, first by landing a capsule on the surface of the Moon and then by photographing the hidden far side.

Space Probes

Each nation has launched one. Our Pioneer V went aloft on March 11, 1960, heading toward the orbit of Venus. It carried instruments to measure radiation in space, including cosmic and solar radiation, and also was intended to study magnetic fields in space and meteorite activity. It continued to transmit scientific data back to Earth for more than three months, and set a long-distance communication record when it transmitted data from a distance of 22,500,000 miles. It is now in orbit around the Sun.

The Soviet space probe was launched on February 12, 1961, and is one of the most phenomenal accomplishments of the space era thus far. It was done in two steps—first, the launching of a "heavy" satellite of unannounced weight, which went into orbit around the Earth and, then, sometime during its first day aloft, launched a 1400-pound rocket *itself*. Using a satellite as a rocket launching station is unique at this time. The rocket was aimed for the planet Venus on a two-month journey, passing close to that world at the end of April.

The firing was doubly significant. Not only did it—in Russia's words—"blaze the first path to planets of the solar system," but it indicated that the Russians are making vast strides in the department of precision as well as in power. American experts guessed that the thrust needed to put the initial rocket into orbit was at least 800,000 pounds, or double the power of the biggest U.S. rocket in operation in 1961. And the technique of launching a rocket from an orbiting satellite requires remote-control guidance systems of incredible precision. The fact that the Russian Venus probe achieved such success demonstrates continued Soviet progress in electronics as well as in rocket-fuel research.

Navigation Satellites

In this phase of space operation we stand unchallenged. While Russia has concentrated on its space probes and heavy satellites, we have worked hard on highly specialized satellites of great practical value, and in some fields we are years ahead of our rivals.

Our navigation-satellite program calls for the launching of four satellites that will facilitate sea and air navigation in all weather. By measuring fluctuations in the frequency of radio signals emanating from a navigation satellite, an observer on Earth can take a "fix" in his position with the utmost accuracy even when clouds are blanketing the ancient navigational aids of the heavens. Two trial satellites of this sort, Transit I and Transit II, were launched in April and June of 1960, as forerunners of the eventual system. The Transit II launching was notable because it carried a piggyback satellite into orbit, the 42-pound Greb satellite, intended to report on the Sun's ultraviolet and X-ray output. It was the first time that two satellites had been launched into separate orbits by the same rocket carrier.

Weather-Observation Satellites

Here, again, there is no known Soviet research, while we are well under way with our program. Our weather satellites are known as TIROS, short for "Television Infrared Observation Satellite." TIROS I, orbited on April 1, 1960, had a spectacularly successful active life of 78 days, during which time it sent more than 20,000 photos of cloud formations back to ground stations. It remains in orbit, but is no longer transmitting. TIROS II, launched six months later, continued the program. Future TIROS satellites will be able to observe and relay reports of threatening weather formations, thus enabling far more accurate prediction of storms than is possible at present. The sensitive detectors and camera mechanisms of the TIROS satellites indicate the advanced state of American optical research, which is probably far beyond current Russian capabilities.

Spy Satellites

This aspect of space research is shrouded in deepest secrecy. The existence of Soviet spy satellites has been frequently rumored, but none have ever been detected by Western observers, and certainly the Russians have never announced publicly any such launchings.

We have a fairly advanced spy-satellite program under way, but little definite news has emerged. The U.S. Air Force has launched well over a dozen satellites in its "Discoverer" series. These have had a variety of test purposes, largely related to perfecting other phases of our space program, and it is believed that at least some of the Discoverer satellites have been preliminary shots for observation satellites.

Two different observation programs are under way. On May 24, 1960, a MIDAS satellite was orbited under a cloak of secrecy, and all that is known about it is that its function is to detect missile launching by heat indication. A related satellite known as SAMOS I was launched the following winter, and is possibly taking photos of Soviet military installations, but a tight security veil has been drawn over its operation. Beyond a doubt, this country is actively proceeding on a series of observation satellites that will circle the Earth and which will make obsolete the manned U-2 overflights that stirred up such controversy in 1960. And it is reasonable to assume that the Soviet Union has a spy-satellite program in the works as well, though quite likely not so far along as ours.

Communications Satellites

This is still another field where the United States thus far has a monopoly of positive accomplishments. While there are no known Russian ventures along this line, we have moved in several paths. Our first success was the 1958 Atlas which carried out the first broadcast from space. Two 1960 satellites indicated varying approaches: the Echo I, a giant balloon that served as a passive communications satellite off whose aluminized skin messages can be bounced, and Courier I, an active communications satellite that received messages from Earth, stored them, and rebroadcast them when over other areas. Both active and passive communications satellites will ultimately be used to improve world-wide telephone communications and to make global TV transmission possible. The American Telephone & Telegraph Company has already announced its intention to launch its own communications satellites within the next few years.

Man Into Space

The goal of all this space research is to extend the domain of humanity into the universe—which means not only to thrust metal probes outward, but eventually to send human beings themselves to the Moon, to the planets, and perhaps even to the stars.

The United States established its formal man-into-space program on October 5, 1958, placing it under the control of the newly created National Aeronautics and Space Administration. The NASA has jurisdiction over those parts of our space program which are primarily civilian and scientific—for instance, the TIROS weather satellites, the Pioneer V space probe, and the communications satellites. But by far the biggest job that fell to Dr. T. Keith Glennan, first head of NASA, was Project Mercury—putting a man into orbit around the Earth and returning him safely to Earth.

Although as early in the space age as 1959 this country developed the capability to launch space satellites with predictable regularity, the obstacles facing Project Mercury were far greater than those confronting satellite launchers. We could put a Discoverer or an Explorer into orbit *most* of the time—our batting average became surprisingly good after a while—but failure in a manned orbital attempt would mean, not merely the loss of equipment, but the loss of a valuable human life. Furthermore, we could not simply thrust a man into orbit and leave him there, as the Russians did with their space-dog Laika; we had to make provisions for his safe return from orbit.

The round trip requirement involved important technological breakthroughs. It was necessary to develop remote-control equipment far beyond anything we had at the time. It was necessary to perfect foolproof rocket devices for returning our astronaut to Earth. And one of the knottiest problems of all was that of re-entry—the problem of coping with the fierce heat that is generated when a fast-moving body enters our atmosphere from space. Unless we wanted to turn our astronauts into shooting stars that would blaze momentarily in the night sky and descend as cinders, much work had to be done.

There was also the human element. Who was to ride a rocket into space, make the perilous orbiting trip, and return?

The NASA set out to deal with its problems in sequence. The McDonnell Aircraft Corporation of St. Louis was assigned the task of designing and building the capsule in which our first astronaut would make his orbital trip. The Atlas missile, a product of the General Dynamics Corporation, was chosen as the rocket that would carry the astronaut into orbit. Thousands of smaller electronics companies were taken on as subcontractors to supply equipment to McDonnell and General Dynamics.

And the astronauts were chosen.

The NASA had a very specific type of man in mind for this biggest of adventures, and the requirements they issued were rigid ones. The volunteers for the Project Mercury job had to be military test pilots with jet credentials and 1500 hours or more of flight time. They had to be graduates of test-pilot schools. They had to be engineers. They had to be under 40. They had to be no taller than five feet eleven.

Above all, they had to be ready for what might very well be a suicide mission.

Despite the highly categorized qualifications, over a hundred men volunteered for the astronaut assignment.

NASA interviewed 69 of these, picking 32 for close examination. After months of rigorous physical and mental testing, seven men were picked, the now-famous Mercury Astronauts. Their names were Cooper, Grissom, Slayton, Carpenter, Schirra, Shepard, and Glenn. Three came from the Air Force, three from the Navy. One was a Marine.

The program called for a two-step conquest of space. The first manned shot would be a simple non-orbital ballistic firing, the NASA decided: an astronaut would be boosted 100 miles into space by an Army Redstone rocket, remain weightless in his space capsule for a few minutes, and then fall back to Earth, landing in the Atlantic. The ballistic firing would give the astronaut experience with actual weightlessness and acceleration, though the maximum speed to be reached would be nothing like the speed needed to enter orbit.

After the ballistic firing test, the next step planned was an actual orbiting: the astronaut's capsule would become a satellite of Earth and would circle the planet a number of times before returning to Earth. This would be the second step in the man-into-space program—to be followed by further orbiting flights, and eventually a journey to the Moon.

Before a human life could be risked, however, a stringent test program had to be carried out, embracing every phase of the operation from blastoff to return. The first factor to be considered is escape from the rocket in case of a firing malfunction. The capsule designers worked out a method whereby if anything went wrong with the launching rocket, the Mercury capsule would blast free of the booster and parachute into the sea. This mechanism had its first test in January, 1960, when a Little Joe solid-fuel rocket was fired at the Wallops Island, Virginia testing base. The Little Joe carried a Mercury capsule equipped for escape, and riding in the capsule was a six-pound rhesus monkey named Miss Sam.

At 36,500 feet, the escape rocket ignited and carried the capsule 250 feet to the right of its launching rocket within a second's time. A parachute blossomed, carrying capsule and monkey safely down to the Atlantic. Although Miss Sam had experienced an acceleration of fourteen gravities going up, she emerged from the capsule grinning and frisky.

Other tests were designed to check on the accuracy of the landside tracking stations, to determine the capsule's resistance to heat, and to perfect the 63-foot nylon parachute that is used to ease the capsule's descent. All during 1960 a series of monkeys and chimps attained brief fame as our latest spacefarers, as test succeeded test, as time drew near for the first orbital shot.

Rocket research continued as well. The Atlas missile chosen for the Mercury firing has a thrust of 360,000 pounds—less than half that of the Russian rockets. But American rockets are on the drawing boards now that will enable the astronauts of tomorrow to make their trips in comparative safety and ease.

One of our super-boosters is the Saturn, under the aegis of Wernher von Braun—a massive cluster of eight engines that will provide a thrust of a million and a half pounds when it becomes operational, some time about 1964. Even more imposing—and further in the future—is the Nova, a titanic rocket that will stand 220 feet high and which will boast a thrust of *six million* pounds—enough to land men on the Moon and bring them back. With the development of these super-rockets, much of today's blastoff anxieties will disappear.

The Russians were far from inactive while work proceeded on Project Mercury. They had their own man-into-space program under way, and their lead in booster thrust gave them an impressive head start.

It was Russia, after all, that had put the first living creature into space—Laika, in 1957. (All subsequent Russian test flights were also made with dogs, rather than monkeys and chimps. Russian space scientists claim dogs are better test subjects.) But Laika was sent on a one-way journey. There was no thought of returning her to Earth.

In the summer of 1958, two more space dogs went up in a rocket—not in orbit, this time, but simply *up*. The rocket reached a height of 280 miles, and the payload, containing the dogs, returned safely to Earth by parachute. We followed this exploit with one of our own, in May, 1959, when two monkeys named Able and Baker traveled 300 miles spaceward in the nose cone of a Jupiter rocket. Both returned alive and unharmed from their trip, though Able died shortly after the journey through a surgical mishap while an electrode was being removed from her body.

Twice in July, 1959, the Russians sent dogs to high altitudes, throwing a rabbit in for good measure on the second trip. This time, the Soviets let us know that they had been doing a good deal of this sort of experimentation in recent years, and that one of their dogs had made four successful trips already.

The next space traveler was an American-fired monkey named Sam—not to be confused with Miss Sam, who was used in the capsule-escape test. Sam and his capsule were returned successfully by parachute from a height of 55 miles in December, 1959.

The following year saw the Russians making impressive strides toward putting a man into space. The first move came on May 15, 1960, when Sputnik IV was launched—the first Sutnik in two years, years in which the Reds had concentrated on non-orbiting projects. Sputnik IV was a giant satellite even by Russian standards, weighing five tons, and the Russian news agency declared that it included a pressurized cabin "carrying a weight equivalent to that of a man . . . and necessary equipment for a future flight by a man." The Russians had planned to return this satellite to Earth, by touching off a rocket with a remote radio control. The signal was sent on May 19, four days after the launching, but the cabin was in the wrong position and, instead of slowing the Sputnik, the rockets accelerated it. In one of their rare announcements of failure, the Soviets admitted that the rocket could not be returned to Earth, but had simply been shifted into a different orbit. It broke up about two months later.

This failure was duly atoned for on August 19, when Sputnik V went into orbit—130 pounds heavier than its huge predecessor. On board were two dogs, Strelka and Belka, along with an assortment of rats, mice, insects, and bacteria for experimental purposes.

According to the Soviet announcement, the satellite was commanded to descend during its 18th orbital spin around the Earth. Shortly afterward, the cabin separated from its booster and began the descent. At a height of about five miles, the capsule containing the animals was ejected from the cabin and came to Earth by parachute, landing almost exactly where the Russians had predicted. "The deviation from the calculated spot amounted to some ten kilometers," they declared, awing American experts who knew how difficult it was to ascertain in advance the flight of a parachuted capsule.

This was the first time living beings had been sent into orbit and then recovered. Only a few days earlier, we had scored two recovery coups of our own. On August 10, a Discoverer satellite had ejected a capsule of instruments that was recovered from the sea. Eight days later, another instrument capsule was ejected from another Discoverer satellite, and this time specially equipped airplanes circling the recovery area made a startling midair snatch as the capsule plummeted toward the water.

Russia experienced failure in its next recovery test, on December 1, 1960. Once again, two dogs were sent into orbit, but recovery attempts went astray, and the dogs perished on return. This unexpected development apparently caused a slowdown in the Russian man-into-space program, which otherwise might have resulted in a Soviet orbital manned flight before the inauguration of President Kennedy.

Three months passed before another of the colossal Sputniks went aloft. This time, on March 9, 1961, recovery was once again on schedule. A dog named Chernushka was sent into orbit and brought back safely. The fifth of the five-ton Sputniks went up only a few weeks later, on March 25, and for the third time recovery was accomplished, a dog named Zvezdochka joining the growing list of the U.S.S.R.'s four-legged astronauts.

Three successful shots out of five brought the Russians into striking distance for making the first manned flight. Rumor and denial emerged repeatedly during March of 1961, and in April the Russians succeeded. A 27-year-old Russian Air Force Pilot, Major Yuri Alekseyevich Gagarin, went aloft on April 12, 1961, and spent 108 minutes in an orbital flight around the Earth. Major Gagarin, the father of two, told listeners on the ground during his flight that he could see the Earth clearly through his portholes, and upon landing said, "I feel fine and I have no injuries or bruises."

The history-making first space flight was another blow to U.S. prestige, though hardly an unexpected one. Few informed Americans had seriously hoped that we could beat the Russians into space. The weight of Gagarin's space capsule was five tons—five times as heavy as the Mercury capsule we are planning to orbit late this year or early in 1962—indicating once again the decisive superiority of Russian booster power.

Major Gagarin's flight, in the spaceship Vostok (*East*), touched off wild celebrations throughout the Communist world, while Americans hid their disappointment and offered well-deserved congratulations. At Langley Air Force Base, the American astronauts in training for a similar flight shrugged away their regrets and buckled down even harder for the time when they could attempt to equal the Russian feat.

Of the original seven, three—John Glenn, Virgil Grissom, and Alan Shepard—were alerted to ready themselves for space flight. From their number, one man would be chosen to make the initial ballistic flight that would be the first American step into space. The other two—and the four men making up our "second team"—would be used in later space shots.

What kind of men were these, from whom our first astronaut was ultimately chosen? John Glenn, Virgil Grissom, Alan Shepard—their names are ordinary American names. Perhaps we can try to take a close look at the first American spacemen, and attempt to understand the sort of personality that would volunteer for such a shot into the dark.

Chapter Four

LIEUTENANT COLONEL JOHN GLENN

John Herschel Glenn, Junior, is the oldest member of the original group of seven Mercury Astronauts—he is just short of forty—and is the only member of the Marine Corps in the group. A relaxed and jovial man externally, Glenn is in reality hard-driving and unbending in his desire to become the perfect spaceman. Everything he does is aimed toward that goal.

The outward Glenn is unremarkable. He stands 5'10½"; his weight, when he was picked for Project Mercury, was over 180, but a stern regimen of diet and exercise has trimmed him down to a lean 165. (Every pound of needless fat that goes up in the Mercury capsule makes the flight that much harder for the booster rocket.) His reddish hair is thinning rapidly. His eyes are green.

Glenn is a family man. His wife, Anna, grew up with him in New Concord, Ohio—they were playmates from the age of 6 on—and the bonds between them are strong. They have two teen-age children—Dave, 15, who takes a keen interest in rocketry and who may be a spaceman himself someday, and Lyn, who is 14. They make their home in Arlington, Virginia.

But, characteristic of Glenn's single-minded devotion to the space project, he lives now in bachelor quarters at Langley Air Force Base in Hampton, Virginia, seeing his family only on weekends. "I could have moved the whole family to Langley, I guess," Glenn says. "But Dave and Lyn were going to a good school, and I didn't want to uproot them." Another reason for the separation is Glenn's preference for having no family distractions during his rigorous training program. Astronauts are kept busy in many ways during their working week, since they not only have to drill themselves into physical perfection but to remain up to date on the latest technical developments in astronautics and rocket theory.

Glenn's wife has no objections to the role of weekday widow. She thinks it's best for him to be alone during his training program—so that he can wrestle with the problems of breaching the space frontier without having to worry about minor household matters at the same time.

Religion is an important factor in Glenn's life. He has said repeatedly that he doesn't think religion should be a sometime thing, an aid in time of emergency only. When he was first being considered for Project Mercury, he and his wife had some doubts about the religious aspects of a human assault on the heavens. Anna Glenn took the matter up with their friend and family minister, the Reverend Frank Erwin, who reassured her that there were no religious blocks standing in the way of man's space program, and certainly no reasons why God would not want John Glenn, in particular, to make the attempt.

Off the job—that is, when he's home at Arlington for the weekend—Glenn tries to relax. But Project Mercury is never very far from his mind, and he'll frequently speak of his experiences during the week just ended, discussing snags and delays in the program with his family.

He lists his hobbies as boating and water-skiing. His friends praise him for his abilities as a conversationalist and storyteller, and it's said that he has a fairly good amateur tenor voice. But hobbies play only a minor role in John Glenn's life. His main interests are his family and his space career—and, for the past two years, it has been difficult to tell which has taken priority.

With furious self-discipline, Glenn has turned himself from a man in above-average physical condition to one in the absolute prime of shape. The Project Mercury program calls for plenty of special exercise, but, strictly on his own, Glenn has expanded his physical training schedule. He runs two miles every morning before breakfast, swims strenuously, watches his diet with an eagle's eye. When he gets the opportunity, he goes water-skiing. He knows that the human factor will be important in space flights, that he must be ready to handle himself in any emergency resulting from mechanical failure, and he wants his body to be keyed for lightning response. As an NASA official put is, "Glenn, like the others, wants to come back alive. And even though our instruments are pretty damn good, they aren't perfect. So Glenn wants to be perfect himself. He wants to be able to make a manual landing under the roughest of conditions—and that calls for phenomenal reflexes."

Glenn is a skilled pilot. He saw combat duty in World War II, served again in Korea and, since the end of hostilities there, has been a test pilot handling our most advanced military jets. He sees his job in space as just an extension of his piloting experience—a mighty extension, true, but nothing that will be beyond his capabilities. Like many modest and humble men, Glenn neither underrates nor overrates his ability. False confidence can be deadly to a test pilot—but so is needless self-downgrading. In an emergency situation, they must be neither foolhardily cocky nor self-pityingly panicky. Glenn is neither.

His flight record totals 5000 hours, giving him the most extensive flying experience of any of the astronauts. 1500 of those hours were spent flying jets, a figure exceeded by some of the younger men. His particular specialty in Project Mercury (each of the astronauts has devoted himself to working on a single aspect of the operation) has been the design of the pilot space in the capsule. Each of the astronauts has made suggestions for increasing the efficiency of the capsule, but none has paid more careful attention to capsule refinement, none has searched more assiduously for hidden flaws and pitfalls, than John Glenn.

The picture takes shape: a man of almost forty, happily married, father of two fine children, skilled and respected in his profession. Why would he volunteer for the dangerous Mercury mission? What forces have driven John Glenn toward his rendezvous with the void?

A sense of duty, primarily. The space frontier is *there*. We are striving to conquer it. There may be grave consequences to our national security as well as to our national pride if we fail to meet the challenge of the space frontier.

Someone, then, must face the risk. Space needs its

Columbuses. We who go through our everyday routines, who strive for family security, who yearn for a new car and a vacation in Europe someday—we are not meant to be Columbuses of space. But some men are. John Glenn is. And he knows it, and that knowledge drives him on. If he had declined the challenge, he would have had to live out his days with the knowledge that he had failed his country in time of need.

Duty, then, motivates John Glenn. He has the training, as a test pilot, that a spaceman can build on. He has the engineering skills. He has the serenity of purpose, the single-mindedness, that any Columbus must have. He has a valuable fund of experience in tight situations, an experience that makes him a prime candidate for the shot into space. With all these qualifications, Glenn must have seen that he had no choice but to make himself available for Project Mercury. The search for security and comfort is not all there is to existence. A man must live with his own conscience—and John Glenn's conscience told him that he was born to be a spaceman.

Of course, Glenn is motivated, as are the other Mercury Astronauts, by more than a solemn-faced Boy Scout kind of duty to one's country. Glenn responds to the excitement of the space plunge. "I'm lucky," he says, "to be around right now, here at the beginning of the space age."

He regards the 1960's as one of the most exciting eras in human history, and he feels a powerful surge of satisfaction at the thought that the chance has been given him to ride in the forefront of the wave of adventure. Great adventures do not fall to every generation of humanity. But one has fallen to ours—and John Glenn is eager to respond to the challenge. "The dare of the future," he calls it.

Beyond the glamour and excitement of Project Mercury, another factor influences Glenn: curiosity. Ever since he was a child, his wife recalls, he had to *find out*. "Insatiable" is the word she uses to describe it. He had to know, to experience, to see for himself.

Glenn's family recognizes this need in him. He is close to the three of them, they know him, and they understand that no family tie could hold him back with space beckoning to him. Wife, son, daughter, all take a deep interest in his training progress, and all hope that he will eventually reach the goal toward which he has aimed so long.

There is danger, yes. There is always danger on the frontiers. Columbus, sailing rashly toward the place where the sea tumbled over the world's edge, faced danger. Orville and Wilbur Wright, skidding through the air in their flimsy planes, courted danger. John Glenn lives daily with danger.

Glenn—and the members of his family—understand that there are two sorts of people, the play-it-safe sort that makes up the majority, and the risk takers. And they recognize that Glenn is a risk-taker, that this is his nature, that this is what he *must* be.

Glenn is no daredevil. "He's not the kind who would be a stunt driver or a tightrope walker or anything like that," an associate says of him. "He doesn't believe in taking chances just for the sake of taking chances. He's not a thrill-seeker. He's in Project Mercury because he sees it as a job to be done, because he sees great personal satisfaction in doing the job, and because he knows his country —and mankind—has to get up and out there."

Glenn will readily admit that space awes him. People who don't know him well sometimes tend to think of him as unimaginative, as a cheerful family man of little depth or complication, but the true Glenn stands in respectful awe of the challenge of space. Diligent and efficient man that he is, he has done his best to eradicate this sensation of awe, out of fear that it may hamper his performance in space. (Psychologists have seriously speculated that the early spacemen may be so dumb-struck by the majesty and splendor of space that they will become unable to function.)

Glenn has gone out of his way to attend every missile firing he could at Cape Canaveral, in a dogged attempt to attain a "so-what" attitude toward the conquest of space. Time and again, he has watched a giant Atlas or Thor rocket blastoff, hoping to wear away by constant repetition the tingle that even the most hardened missile man still experiences. How successful he has been at this attempt to reduce man's greatest adventure to manageable proportions, Glenn will not say.

He felt neither exultation nor apprehension on that day

in February, 1961, when Robert Gilruth, director of the NASA's Space Task Group, told him that he had been chosen as one of the trio from whom the first rocket rider would ultimately be chosen. Realistic, practical, Glenn attaches less importance to "being *first*" than do some of his fellow astronauts. Naturally, he would welcome the honor if it fell to him—but he knows that all seven of the astronauts will have their turn in space, their day of glory, and that the important part of the operation is not *who* gets there but that we get there at all.

Glenn takes an equally hardheaded attitude about Russain space accomplishments. Disappointed but unsurprised by Yuri Gagarin's orbital flight, Glenn was well aware of the propaganda coup scored by the Soviet Union. But he didn't feel that we should have raced to beat the Russians into space at the cost of taking risks. He's much more interested in doing a thorough job of preparation, in making a successful and fruitful flight instead of a hasty one. He sees the entire Project Mercury operation as something more noble than a mere propaganda stunt.

"A lot of people," comments a Defense Department official, "seem to take the attitude that the only point of our space program is to keep the Russians from getting there first. As John Glenn of the astronaut bunch has pointed out, that's a pretty short-sighted and foolish way to look at things. We're going up there to *learn*. We want to find out what the universe is like, and we want to carve a foothold for ourselves up there. The propaganda angles are important, but secondary in the long run. The way Glenn sees this project, we don't know what we're likely to find out there, but we're going to find *something*—and that's why he plans to be in that capsule."

A smiling, freckled man, brave and patriotic, Glenn has been risking his life for his country as a matter of almost daily routine for nearly twenty years. He has faced the risks squarely, and has decided they are worth the taking.

Glenn frankly admits that he would probably have a better life expectancy in some other line of endeavor. "But with risks you gain," says John Glenn. As he readied himself for the call to duty that might come at any moment, as, night after night, he went mentally through the visualization of himself climbing into the capsule and waiting, there on the launchng pad, for the great upward thrust—as he waited for the final countdown that might make him the first American into space, John Glenn knew that the risks were great—but that he and his country had a universe to gain.

Chapter Five

CAPTAIN VIRGIL GRISSOM

Shortest and youngest of the three-man astronaut final team, Captain Virgil Ivan ("Gus") Grissom of the Air Force hardly looks like a hero. A stubby, stocky man who carries 155 pounds on a 5'7" frame, the 35-year-old Grissom looks more like a high school gym teacher or a hi-fi repairman than a space pioneer.

But a quiet competence is the hallmark of this soft-spoken, amiable, and relaxed man. He has no power urge, no desire to make himself a celebrity. He realizes that national fame may very well be thrust upon him, but it will be through none of his own doing. He sees himself simply as a man doing his job. He has no mystique of duty, like John Glenn; to Grissom, space flight is all in a day's work.

In keeping with this attitude, he tends to underplay everything concerned with Project Mercury. He scoffs at any attempt to compare the astronauts to earlier adventurers like Columbus, Lindbergh, the Wright Brothers. He stresses the point that they were all solitary figures who carried out their dreams in the teeth of bitter opposition, making an uphill struggle of it all the way—while the Mercury Astronauts are simply passengers in a capsule originated, developed, and pushed through to completion by other men.

Grissom's modesty about his big role in the space age is excessive, perhaps, but it isn't a pose. He's a genuinely self-effacing, unheroic man who takes the low-pressure view of himself and of the world around him.

Gus Grissom was born in Mitchell, Indiana. He was a member of the Boy Scouts, and, shortly after his selection as one of the Mercury team, a reporter hunted up his old scoutmaster for a comment. The scoutmaster reportedly was surprised to hear that Grissom would volunteer for a mission of this sort. All his life, the cool-nerved, even-tempered Grissom has given this impression of not really being an adventurous type.

But he himself quietly denies it, pointing out his child-hood adventures on solo trips through caves and stone quarries as examples of his love of exploration.

Grissom has been married since 1945, when he was still in his teens, and is the father of two sons, Mark, 7, and Scott, 10. During World War II he was trained as an air cadet, but had no actual flight experience. At the war's end, he took a job with a company that produced school buses—but it was immediately clear both to him and to his wife, Betty, that this wasn't the kind of thing he wanted to do.

He enrolled at Purdue University in 1946 to study mechanical engineering. Betty Grissom has none-too-fond memories of those college days, when they lived in a single room and attempted to scrape along on his GI Bill payments and her earnings as a telephone operator. (She worked a 5 to 11 shift to keep out of his way while he studied.) After graduation, he discovered no attractive jobs available, and so he returned to the Air Force as a cadet. Finances became a problem after the birth of their first son in 1950, but somehow they made do on his $130 a month pay.

During the Korean War, Grissom flew a hundred combat missions in Sabre-jets. (Jet flying accounts for 2000 of the 3000 flight hours to his credit.) He regards his experiences in dueling with Communist MiGs as a valuable toughening-up for his later space career. In this baptism under fire at 600 miles an hour, he learned how to stand up to stress situations, how to remain calm and collected with death only a trigger burst away. In his hundred missions, he emerged unharmed and with a new, more solid appreciation of his own competence under fire.

"And it was a lot safer being shot at than teaching air cadets how to fly," Grissom told his wife. He insists that flying is less hazardous than driving an auto—you have complete control, and you don't need to worry about drunken drivers making unexpected swerves.

In his career as a combat pilot and later as a test pilot, Grissom had only one serious accident. Oddly, his companion on that occasion was Gordon Cooper, another of the original seven Mercury Astronauts, though the incident took place years before either man had any idea he was destined to be a spaceman. On that occasion Grissom and Cooper were in a T-33 jet whose landing gear collapsed on take-off. The jet crashed and burned, but both men escaped injury.

Grissom's undemonstrative, self-possessed attitude of confidence took him through a series of test-flying exploits in the post-Korea years. He specialized in testing the unusual and the unpredictable, and on at least one instance carried out a successful test even though some people around him regarded the mission as "downright suicidal."

Grissom generally keeps the details of his progress as an astronaut to himself, unlike the more outgoing John Glenn, who shares every experience with his family. Grissom simply believes that his wife is more interested in *him* than in his work, and though he keeps her informed on important developments, he makes no attempt to unburden himself of every problem that arises during the testing and development program. The Grissoms live in Newport News, Virginia, some seventeen miles from the Langley Air Force Base.

Again in contrast to John Glenn, Gus Grissom has no formal and intensive schedule of physical exercise. He keeps in shape, but without such formidable tasks as Glenn's daily two-mile run. Grissom limbers up by hunting and fishing; he enjoys a frequent bike ride; and he keeps his hands strong by squeezing a spring exerciser. He is a first-rate handball player, and would be undefeated in Astronaut handball competition but for the time he lost a single game to the third member of the final team, Alan Shepard. "The only reason Gus lost," another astronaut has suggested, "is that he knew Al wanted to win so badly."

But this joking explanation probably has little basis in fact. For all his outward modesty and casual self-deprecation, Grissom has an astronaut's pride, and is hardly likely to have deliberately thrown a game, even of handball, for any reason whatever. Grissom likes to win. He makes no fuss about his competitive instinct, but he resents being shrugged off as a man without the victory drive. He keeps it under wraps, but he is as fiercely bent on achievement, whether in handball or in astronautics, as any member of the team.

The counterbalance of his quiet self-confidence is a kind of self-doubt, a steady feeling of surprise at his own accomplishments. Like many short men, he sometimes gives way to a feeling that the "big boys" can outperform him. In the end, he finds, he equals or tops anyone else's performance, but he is always surprised.

Grissom has made a sober appraisal of the dangers that lie ahead for the Mercury Astronauts on their orbiting trips. His particular specialty in the project is the automatic control system that will guide the capsule as it heads back to Earth after the orbiting flight. His one special worry is that this system will fail. The astronaut will then have to guide the capsule down manually, instead of depending on a mechanical "brain" that would automatically correct for any deviations in the capsule's downward journey.

A manual descent would be a grim test of an astronaut's piloting skill. He'll be holding a stick that will control jets that he can fire to correct course deviations. An overcorrection can lead to a fatal spin. The capsule will be uncomfortably warm, and the pilot will be experiencing a double gravitational drag as the capsule drops—but a miscue that sends the capsule tumbling could lead to a fiery death.

The blunt nose of the capsule will be shielded against heat, and this shielded nose must be kept straight down during the descent. Maintaining the same angle of descent under manual control will be a tricky job, and Grissom —who has studied this aspect more intensively than any of his colleagues—has reason to hope that when he finally makes an orbiting flight he won't be called on to use his piloting savvy during re-entry.

But Grissom has faith in his ability to stay cool under

circumstances that could cause panic. During the elimination period, when the seven Mercury Astronauts were being chosen, he, like all the other candidates, was confronted with a demonic test device unfondly called the Idiot Box. This was a specially gimmicked instrument panel designed to test co-ordination under stress. Each instrument had its own operating instructions; some had knobs to be pushed, others switches to be flipped, still others, handles to be yanked or turned. A fast-action sequence of colored lights flashed at random over the board, and the candidate had to put out the lights by pushing the proper button, yanking the right handle, flipping the right switch. If he lagged more than a fraction of a second behind par, a horn would screech behind his ear.

Grissom handled the Idiot Box with no more difficulty than most men have in driving a car. Having come through that particular test ordeal, he is not overly terrified of the possible mishaps that might befall him in a Mercury orbital flight.

As always, the question of *Why?* is a vital one in trying to know these spacemen. What drives them to volunteer for a task like this?

Gus Grissom offers no fancy explanations. He believes he's qualified, and he has never turned his back on a job he thought he could handle. Like his colleagues, he responds to the importance of the conquest of space, and relishes the thought of getting in on the ground level.

Certainly he is not out for personal prestige. Career advancement, yes; he knows that his part in the Mercury program has marked him for even bigger roles in the future, and he sees that as all to the good. He's not interested in bogging down at a fixed position; so long as the Air Force offers him room to grow, he intends to take advantage.

His wife takes a level-headed approach toward the entire assignment. When the idea of Project Mercury first was broached to him, Betty Grissom says she fretted more about the effect on him if he were turned down than about the risks involved in making the flight. She knows better than anyone else how eager he is to take on new challenges, and she feared he'd take it badly to be rejected.

And at one point it did seem as though he'd be refused. Grissom has hay fever. After he had passed through the early stages of the elimination trials, a doctor examining him learned about the hay fever allergy and said, "That just about washes you out of this project right now."

But Grissom insisted that hay fever would make no difference. He'd be sealed into a pressurized cabin, he argued, and no ragweed pollen would get sealed in with him. And certainly he wasn't likely to inhale any out in space.

He won his point and, after some time of doubt, was allowed to continue in the testing program. "I was every bit as happy as he was," Betty Grissom says.

If she has any fears for her husband's safety, they aren't visible. It has to be remembered that all of the astronauts are veteran test pilots, and their wives have long since become accustomed to the risks. Discussing the Mercury orbital shot with her, Grissom told Betty that he was positive he'd come through it safely, and that he'd never let anyone launch him into orbit until he was certain he was coming back. She has accepted that flat statement and has ceased to worry about the possibilities.

Grissom himself has a businesslike approach. He expects to be scared when he boards the capsule, but he's not worried about it. Once the flight begins, he knows, he'll have too many things to do to have time to worry. He's been through it before—on that earlier test mission that some people thought was "downright suicidal"—and his worries evaporated when the time came for testing.

Since 1958, he has known that the odds on his becoming the first American into space were seven to one. After the odds narrowed to three to one in February of 1961, Grissom continued to take the same unsensationalized, unemotional attitude toward the forthcoming flight. Without minimizing for a moment the importance and wonder of a journey into space, he plays down his own part in the enterprise, and gives himself no hero's laurels. He simply settled down to wait, knowing that there was one chance in three that he would be picked for that first ride out of the world, and intending to do his usual capable job if the nod went to him.

Chapter Six

COMMANDER ALAN SHEPARD

Each of the three members of the final team is sharply different from the others in personality. John Glenn is a middle-of-the-roader, hard-working, genial, uncomplicated. Virgil Grissom is unassuming, quiet, self-contained. Alan Shepard, who holds the rank of Commander in the United States Navy, seems more complex than either of the other two men—quick-witted, energetic, almost flamboyantly brilliant. At the risk of punning, it would be accurate to call Shepard *mercurial*.

Shepard is 37, the father of two girls, 13-year-old Laura and nine-year-old Juliana. His wife's niece, nine-year-old Alice Williams, lives with the family. At 5′11″, Shepard is taller than both Grissom and Glenn, and weighs in at a wiry 160 pounds. He moves with loose-jointed ease, and his clothing is always in impeccable taste.

Shepard is a restless man, a prowler, a searcher, a studier. He is considered a hard man to get to know. Behind the outward gaiety and ease of the man, a chilled-steel barricade sometimes interposes, indicating his innate caution and aloofness. Although the seven astronauts have always been looked upon as equals—and have looked upon themselves that way—Shepard has attained a kind of pre-eminence without official standing. His teammates readily admit his keenness of mind and his skills as a pilot, indicating the respect with which he is regarded.

Whereas Virgil Grissom rarely speaks unless he has something he considers vital to say, Shepard sparkles in conversation, easily dominating any group. He has the knack of talking *to* rather than *at* other people, and can hold forth on a wide range of subjects. The one topic he rarely brings into the conversation is himself. A strange reticence comes over this lively animated man whenever discussion becomes at all personal, and he lowers the barricade.

Shepard shares John Glenn's love of water-skiing, but adds his own colorful touch to the hobby. He began in the standard way, using two skis—but as soon as he had become proficient that way, he shifted to using only *one* ski, a vastly more difficult proposition. Now, his wife Louise says, he's looking around for someone with a boat fast enough to tow him *barefoot* over the water. It isn't a daredevil trait in him, Louise Shepard insists; it's merely his restless desire to learn how to do everything, and then do it a little better than most people can.

Shepard is also a sports-car enthusiast. He owns a souped-up white Corvette equipped with racing tires, and often chafes at dull things like speed limits. Project Mercury officials take a poor view of their astronauts being hauled into court for speeding—or, for that matter, of their wrapping themselves around telephone poles at a hundred miles an hour—and so Shepard has been keeping his racing ambitions under wraps. Instead, he fiddles endlessly with the car's engine, lavishing all of his considerable engineering skill on it. On his frequent visits to Cape Canaveral, 800 miles south of his Virginia Beach, Virginia home, he refuses to fly, making the trip in his Corvette instead. (Friends say the travel time is sometimes almost about the same when Shepard gets a clear road ahead of him, but he denies this. He just likes to drive, he says.)

Shepard was born in East Derry, New Hampshire, and attended the U.S. Naval Academy at Annapolis. (He won a varsity letter in crew there.) A qualified test pilot, he couldn't wait to get his flying license and, impatient over Navy delays in issuing him his wings, he attended a civilian flight school in spare hours and got his private license there.

This chafing impatience is one of Alan Shepard's strongest characteristics: he is a man in a hurry. He sees most of the people around him moving too slowly, and he has to force himself to simmer down while waiting for the rest of the world to catch up with him. Probably, if the decision had been put in his own hands, Shepard would have ordered a Mercury flight (with himself in the capsule) months ago. As it is, he's had to wait while the long testing process works its way toward completion.

Like Virgil Grissom—and unlike John Glenn—Shepard follows a policy of keeping Project Mercury out of the family dinner-table conversation. When something big goes wrong— like the performance flaws that marred the unmanned test shot of March 18, 1961,when the escape rocket went off too early and the reserve parachute opened by accident—Shepard is likely to bring the news home to his family. But, by and large, he tries not to talk about the day-by-day ups and downs of the space project. He has said he wants family life going on "normally" at home—which means a soft-pedaling of the constant awareness that the head of the family is likely to be fired out into space on a few hours' notice.

Similarly, he doesn't attempt to explain the project in detail to his wife—but he does spell out for her those aspects of the operation he thinks she might worry about. Actually, Louise Shepard says she does little worrying. A Christian Scientist, she is confident that God will be looking after her husband when his turn comes to ride the nose cone. Her approach to the whole prospect of an orbiting husband is an unflustered and serene one.

Shepard's special area assignment on Project Mercury is to work with the groups charged with the astronaut's recovery. He knows the difficulties involved in making the pickup once the encapsulated astronaut has plummeted down through the atmosphere and landed in the Atlantic. If the re-entry rockets work properly, the astronaut should land fairly close to the predicted impact point, and he'll simply have to wait for the recovery vessels to head for the spot and pick him up. In case it becomes necessary to make a manual landing, though, the capsule may drop into the sea hundreds of miles from the planned impact point.

For that reason, Shepard has given special attention to the perfecting of the world-wide tracking range that will maintain surveillance on the capsule as it descends. Each of the tracking stations will transmit its information to a main computer as the capsule passes overhead, so that rescue ships can be despatched rapidly to the landing area.

Shepard took enthusiastically to the rigorous training of the astronauts, even doing some roadwork after hearing John Glenn singing the praises of his daily run. The hardest part of the training, Shepard says, was the psychological testing. Apparently he dislikes thinking about himself almost as much as he does talking about himself, and he found it difficult to dig into his own motivations and responses as deeply as the tests required him to do.

The result of this attitude is a kind of cool detachment about himself and the project he's involved in. "So far as he's willing to let on," says a man who's as close to Shepard as anyone is, "he's completely nerveless about this whole operation. Of course, it's hard to tell what Al *really* feels. He never lets down his guard. But he gives the impression that he's taking the project completely in his stride."

Shepard, like the others, disclaims all intention of wanting to be a hero. In his own sparse statements on his reasons for volunteering, he simply says that it was a chance for him to serve his country in a role for which he was well qualified—and that it was a personal challenge to him, rather like barefoot water-skiing.

"The way Al looks at it," a friend commented, "is that it would be a kind of treason to himself not to volunteer. That is, he's got the training, he's got the talents this thing needs—and if he doesn't put that unique experience of his to use where it's needed the most, it would be a tremendous waste of a career."

Which is why Alan Shepard gave up the security of his Navy life—which would almost certainly have brought him a squadron command in a few years' time—to volunteer for years of grueling training and a chancy shot into the unknown.

Shepard spends little time "stewing" over the space flights he may be called upon to make. In his typical offhand manner, he admits that it'll be a thrill to ride around the Earth in a space capsule—but then quickly goes on to say that it's more important to know how to handle the capsule's controls than it is to speculate about the glories of space.

Alert, aggressive, impulsive—Alan Shepard is in many ways different from the sternly disciplined John Glenn and the modest, spotlight-shunning Virgil Grissom. He has mastered every aspect of Project Mercury, and he itches to be up there in orbit, as soon as possible. Meanwhile, as the long countdown continues, he tinkers with his sports car, burns up his excess energy with ice-skating and golf, and waits for his big chance to come. Just as once, off the coast of Korea, he lost his radio aids and had to make a carrier landing in darkness and heavy fog (he worried a little, then settled down and made the tricky landing coolly and easily), he looks forward to his first space ride with the knowledge that there'll be dangers involved, that he may be tested to the full limits of his capabilities—but that he'll meet the tests, and ride his capsule safely back to Mother Earth.

Chapter Seven

PROJECT MERCURY'S SECOND TEAM

Seven men were chosen, in 1958, to undergo special training for Project Mercury. More than two years later, in
February, 1961, three of these men—Glenn, Grissom, and
Shepard—were named the "finalists" from whom the first
missile-riding spaceman would be chosen. One of those
three has now actually made a ballistic flight into space.

But the other four men, the "second team" of the astronauts, remain very much a part of the project. They should
be thought of, not as ballplayers sent down to the minor
leagues for more seasoning, but as skilled men standing
just behind the "varsity," ready and able to serve as
needed. Although they were not needed for the first ballistic
flight, their services will be drawn upon as Project Mercury swings into its next phase, the job of getting a man
into permanent orbit. In due time, all four of these men
will join the "first team" as orbiters. Each man has his
special contribution to make to the operation and—aside
from the matter of historical priority in making the first
shot—each can be considered to have played an equally
important role in America's first step into the unknown
universe.

We have looked in some detail at the members of the
three-man Redstone missile launch team from whom our
first space adventurer was picked. But it is important
neither to overlook nor to underestimate the other four
Mercury Astronauts. These are the men who complete the
group that our great-grandchildren will revere as America's
first spacemen:

Scott Carpenter

Lieutenant Malcolm Scott Carpenter of the United States Navy is the only Mercury Astronaut with more than two children—he has four, Scott, Jay, Kristen, and Candace, ranging in age from 11 down to 4. (A fifth child died in infancy ten years ago.) Unlike most of the other selectees, Carpenter has had relatively little jet testing experience, only 300 hours out of his total of 2800. Most of his flying time had been recorded behind the controls of multi-engine propeller aircraft, though he had done some testing of Navy jet fighters.

Because of this—and because he had done virtually no testing of high-performance airplanes for the two years just prior to his selection—Carpenter admits he was a trifle surprised to have been picked as an astronaut. He credits his success to his excellent record in the battery of physiological stress tests given each candidate, rather than to any special skills as a pilot.

Oddly, the Project Mercury assignment rescued Carpenter from a task he considers even more grueling, and one that he was glad to escape from—a two-year tour of duty aboard an aircraft carrier. Every naval officer, whether or not he is given piloting responsibilties, is required to serve regular tours of sea duty, and Carpenter's time had come. He was faced with the prospect of spending long stretches in separation from his family, and—equally irksome—of holding a nonflying job aboard the carrier. Much to his relief, last-minute instructions confirming his selection as a Mercury Astronaut arrived, only hours before his carrier was scheduled to leave San Diego for a cruise of the western Pacific.

Since then, the Colorado-born Carpenter, who is 36, has been an important part of Project Mercury. His particular specialty area is navigation and communications, and he has worked hard on the job of ironing out bugs in the capsule's design that might interfere with the astronaut's communication channels.

Carpenter's wife, Rene, takes a generally unmelodramatic view of her husband's risky profession. She has always been unusually close to him, and has a realistic and accurate idea of the hazards involved. Carpenter tells her in detail of every step in Project Mercury. She once wrote to him, when he had gone to Washington for his first briefing as an astronaut, "I think you were born for this and God knows I'd rather have you in space than at sea. . . . I'm so darned happy and proud for you."

So eager is Rene Carpenter to share her husband's role in space that when, early in the pre-selection testing program, she had a chance to end his participation in the project without his knowledge, she unhesitatingly refused. Carpenter was at sea when a message came from Washington telling him that he had to contact that office by the following Monday or be dropped from consideration. A wife secretly unwilling to have her husband become an astronaut might have destroyed the letter, or perhaps just hidden it till the deadline was past. Rene Carpenter contacted Washington herself to explain the situation, and her husband was not dropped.

With four children, Carpenter is the busiest family man of the group. He's intensely devoted to the children—a devotion heightened by the loss of his six-month-old son in 1951—and spends nearly every hour of his free time playing with them. The 5'10", 160-pound Carpenter lists his hobbies as archery, skindiving, and water-skiing. When away from his family on training missions, he writes long letters to his wife—as many as seventeen pages—describing in detail each stage of the operation, and his hopes and fears for the future.

Neither Scott nor Rene Carpenter claim to be fearless. Carpenter thinks about the orbiting trip a great deal, and is aware of the riskiness of it—but he says repeatedly and with conviction that the conquest of space is an adventure he's willing to give his life for—and he considers himself lucky to have something he can care about so much. Rene Carpenter tells of the time years back when he was a test pilot at Patuxent River, Maryland, and she expected the worst every time he failed to show up by 6 o'clock sharp for dinner. Eventually she found herself reaching the point where she wondered what she'd say to the chaplain when he came to the door to announce the bad tidings.

But—by talking openly of these fears and doubts—both Carpenters have come to terms with danger and spend little time worrying. There are risks, but there are great rewards, too, for a pioneer of space.

Carpenter is frank about his reason for volunteering. Like the others, he felt that he had certain skills to offer, and that he would be derelict in his duty to hold back. But he also openly stresses the desire for immortality. He knows that the names of our first spacemen will be emblazoned on history, and he would very much like one of those names to be his.

One chance to make history has already passed him by, now that another man has made the Redstone test flight. But there are still the orbiting flights yet to come, and he will get his opportunity then to write the name of Malcolm Scott Carpenter in fiery letters across the pages of tomorrow's history books.

Gordon Cooper

Captain Leroy Gordon Cooper, Jr., U.S. Air Force, youngest of the seven, is 34 years old, and the father of two. His wife, Trudy, is a pilot herself—she learned to fly in Hawaii, and she and Cooper joined a flying club soon after they met and explored the Hawaiian Islands in a tiny Piper Cub—and so she is even more hardened to the dangers and joys of leaving Earth behind than the other astronaut wives. (They even took their first baby flying with them soon after she was born.)

Cooper has been flying as long as he could remember. His father, a retired Air Force colonel, was a close friend of such pioneer aviators as Amelia Earhart and Wiley Post, and young Cooper spent nearly as much time up in the air with his father and his friends as he did on *terra firma*. He first handled the controls of a plane when he was about 8, flew his first solo at 16. Joining the Air Force on a career basis was an automatic step for Cooper. As an Air Force pilot, he has racked up 2300 hours in the air, 1400 of them in jets.

He is a self-assured, confident man, who, without any arrogant cockiness, is able to make an objective survey of his own special abilities. He says, for example, that once he had completed his preliminary testing for Project Mercury, he knew he must have won a place in the final seven. With sublime confidence, Cooper returned to Edwards Air Force Base, where he was engaged in testing the new F-106B jet, and told his commanding officer that he would probably need a new test pilot pretty soon. In another man, this kind of talk might have been empty boasting. But Cooper *knew*.

A man of medium build (5'9½", 150 pounds), Cooper is a native of Shawnee, Oklahoma. He has two children, Camala, 12, and Janita, 11. The Coopers are one of the two astronaut families that live at the project headquarters, Langley Air Force Base, in officers' quarters. (The others are the Scott Carpenters.)

Cooper lists his hobbies as photography, riding, hunting, and fishing. He also admits to having had an unabashed interest in space since the days of the early Buck Rogers comic strips and radio programs. (Buck's adventures took place in the 25th Century; young Cooper often wondered impatiently if it would really take six hundred years for men to be flitting from planet to planet.)

As a test pilot, Cooper often found himself flying at great heights, and felt the urge to go just a bit higher, and then just a bit higher yet, until he could look down at the distant green globe of Earth from the vantage point of space itself. Thus, he regards his selection as a Mercury Astronaut as a culmination of many dreams and ambitions.

Pioneering and adventure run in the Cooper bloodstream. The son of a pilot, he's the grandson of bold Oklahoma settlers who ventured into Indian country sixty years ago. (His grandmother is still alive in Shawnee, nearing 90, and she takes a vivid interest in every aspect of the unfolding space age—particularly her grandson's part in it.)

Trudy Cooper doesn't feel that Project Mercury has caused any great dislocation in the life of the Cooper family. The schedule is strenuous, but no more so than his test-piloting schedule of several years back. There were dangers then, and there are dangers now. When the family is together, they spend their time picnicking, swimming, hiking, just as they have always done. As for the space shot itself, Trudy Cooper admits she'll be tense in the moments before blastoff, but she won't be afraid—and she wants to be there to watch it go.

Cooper's special field of responsibility in Project Mercury is the Redstone rocket in which the pre-orbital ballistic shot was made. Since he himself was not picked for the Redstone shot, he was doing his job for the benefit of another man. But he knew that there was only one chance out of seven that he would be the one chosen to ride the Redstone rocket on whose testing he had worked so hard. He has the knowledge that it was his labor that contributed to the ballistic shot, that his many trips to Cape Canaveral to watch test firings paid off in safety for one of his fellow astronauts. The Number One man in the project has won himself a special place in space annals, to be sure—but it's the team accomplishment that put him there.

Besides, Cooper points out, there are going to be many "Firsts" in the space program, and before long each of the Mercury Astronauts will have a "First" of his own. There has already been a first American fired into space. But still to come are the first man to ride in orbit around the Earth, the first to make an orbiting trip around the Moon, the first actually to land on the Moon, the first to reach Mars—there is a universe full of "Firsts" waiting for the spacemen who did not make that first ballistic flight. The Redstone shot was a climax of the first part of our man-into-space program, but, as Cooper and the others know, it signaled not a culmination but a beginning.

Walter Schirra

Easygoing, unflappable Walter Marty Schirra, Junior, who holds the rank of Lieutenant Commander in the U.S. Navy, hides his ambitions and his aggressive nature behind an outward façade of imperturbability and relaxation. "Wally never broods about anything," says his wife, Jo, and his casual, unbrooding approach has seen some of the tenser astronauts through a few of the more anxious moments in the three years of Project Mercury's existence.

Schirra is 38. He was born in Hackensack, New Jersey, and had rolled up thirteen years of flying experience before volunteering for the space program. 1700 of his 3000 accredited flight hours were spent in jets.

When he first learned of Project Mercury, he hesitated for two weeks before volunteering, talking it over with his wife and deciding whether or not he really wanted to go into the project. Neither of them was troubled by the possible danger of the assignment—Schirra has always felt that there was less risk involved in riding a missile into space than there is in trying out an untested jet fighter- -but he was concerned about leavng the jet test program he was involved with. Only when he came to see that Project Mercury was no propaganda stunt, but something of serious importance, did he decide to transfer from jet fighter testing to rocketeering.

Schirra has two children—Marty, 11 and Suzanne, 2. His wife is the stepdaughter of retired U.S. Navy Admiral James L. Holloway. Schirra's career has always kept him away from his family more than he would prefer—only days after the birth of his first child, he was ordered off on a six-month Mediterranean cruise—but, like all the astronauts, he tries to make up for lost time whenever he can return home for some family living. The Schirras make their home in Newport News, Virginia. Schirra's outside interests include sports cars, hi-fi, skiing, and—what seems to be a universal hobby among the Mercury men- -water skiing. At 5'10" he is one of the tallest, and at 185 pounds the heaviest, of the astronauts.

As a fighter pilot in Korea, and as a Navy test pilot after that, Schirra has had plenty of opportunity to experience sudden emergencies. Flying an F-84 jet in Korea, he got his first real taste of Soviet technical prowess when he came in contact with the hard-flying, fast-moving Russian MiG jets, and his combat experience left him with the deep-rooted conviction that we are facing a skilled and able adversary against whom we must expend a maximum effort even if we only hope to maintain the status quo.

After the Korean War, he helped in development of the Sidewinder air-to-air missile, once running into a ticklish situation when a Sidewinder he had fired at a drone airplane got its signals crossed and looped upward toward his own plane. (He looped right along with it, eluding the missile until it ran out of fuel. But the experience helped to show him how mechanical failures can afflict even the most sophisticated of electronic devices, and how human ingenuity is sometimes essential in the tight spots.)

Schirra's particular responsibility on Project Mercury has been in the field of environmental control. That is, he has concentrated on the equipment inside the space capsule that must maintain a livable environment for the astronaut. Such necessities as the pilot's space suit, the air circulation mechanisms, and the air-conditioning units that will cool the capsule during its plunge through the atmosphere have come under Schirra's special scrutiny.

As the project continued from its earliest phases, Schirra's task was to keep particular watch for flaws in the space capsule's control-of-environment systems. Developed along the way, often at his suggestion, were such precautionary devices as a second air-cooling system inside the space suit (in case the main air conditioners fail) and dehumidifiers to deal with pilot perspiration. Once, while testing his suit for waterproofing, Schirra made the mistake of jumping into a pool without his helmet on. The suit filled rapidly with water and Schirra was drawn below the surface. After scrambling out of the pool, the panting Schirra had to be held upside down by Astronauts Glenn and Slayton while the water drained out of his suit. (The incident resulted in a modification of the suit: there's now a neck dam at the suit's top, to keep it from filling with water even when the helmet is off.)

For all his relaxed and cheerful nature, Schirra has made no bones about his desire to be first. He believes that every member of the team feels the same way—no man willing to settle for second place would make a good astronaut, perhaps—but Schirra unhesitatingly voices his wish to reap the harvest of glory that will fall to the first orbiter.

Not that he will consume himself with jealousy if he is passed over for the orbital flight as he was for the preliminary ballistic flight. He feels that the best man will make it, the one who is at the peak of the team, and though he is making every attempt to reach that peak himself, he is willing to concede that one of the others may be better qualified when the time comes for the initial orbiting flight. In that case, Schirra says, he'll regard the man who does go as the representative of the team—and he'll feel not envy but pride at the other man's accomplishments.

Donald Slayton

Captain Donald Kent ("Deke") Slayton of the U.S. Air Force is 37 years old, stands 5'10½", weighs 160 pounds. His family, at the moment, consists of four: himself, his wife, Marjorie, his 4-year-old son, Kent, and a gigantic hundred-pound Weimaraner dog named Acey.

The Slaytons bought Acey in Germany, where Don was stationed and Marjorie was working for the Air Force. Slayton's tender handling of the puppy impressed Marjorie with his gentleness. They were married soon after, spent their honeymoon in Paris, returning to the States so Slayton could attend test pilot school at Edwards Air Force Base.

In his years as a test pilot, Slayton had clocked 3400 hours in the air, 2000 of them in jets, before being tapped for Project Mercury. For three years prior to his space assignment, Slayton had been testing the most advanced jet aircraft, work that he not only found exciting and rewarding in itself but which he regards as an invaluable preparation for the challenges of space flight that lie ahead for him.

He cites, as an example of the sort of thing he became accustomed to, an incident in the $15,000,000 F-105 jet that he had been testing. Decelerating at 38,000 feet, something went wrong and the plane tumbled into an inverted spin. No one had ever piloted an F-105 through an ordinary spin before, let alone an inverted one, so Slayton was forced to improvise—which is what test pilots are sent up to do. He experimented with spin recoveries while the plane continued to plummet dizzily, and finally got control at 10,000 feet.

He was nervous, he says—*after* he got back to solid ground. There was no time to indulge in the luxury of being nervous during the spin itself. Slayton expects to react the same way if any mishap occurs while he's riding an orbital capsule—get things under control first, do his worrying afterward.

Slayton's special area of responsibility on the project has been the Atlas rocket, the booster that will be used on the first orbital flight. As part of his work in this area, Slayton has attended many rocket firings at Cape Canaveral, studying the performance of the big missile that will in the near future hurl him or one of his six colleagues into an orbit around the Earth.

The performance record of the Atlas has been better than expected, to date. But, perhaps more than any of the other astronauts, Slayton knows the chance that something might go astray with one of the mighty rocket's 40,000 parts when the final countdown takes place. Five general areas of potential failure have been isolated, and each gets a careful checkover before any firing. But there is still the definite likelihood of malfunction—of an explosion on the launching pad, of a failure in the early moments of the upward flight—and so Slayton and the Mercury engineers have concentrated on the escape mechanism that will get the man-bearing capsule free of an ill-fated Atlas before it can come to harm. Slayton's chief worry is of a misfire in the first moments. The escape rocket will carry the capsule only 2500 feet up before descent begins, which means the parachute won't have much time to open, and the landing—probably on solid ground—will be a rough one.

Another point Slayton has taken up with the project's co-ordinators involves the reductions of human error. He feels that the less time the astronaut spends in the capsule waiting for blastoff, the less chance there is that fatigue and tension will interfere with his performance aloft. Slayton has pressed for a cut-down in the time the astronaut will have to spend on the ground, and he hopes that it will be no more than forty minutes between the time the capsule is sealed and the time the Atlas goes into action.

Slayton takes the long view of man's progress. Although he always adds that mandatory proviso of the atomic age, "If we don't blow up the world first," he frequently likes to speculate on the future of space exploration. He has a strong sense of being in on the ground floor of a movement that may take mankind out of this solar system within fifty years or so, and which will certainly be the main focus of human endeavor for centuries to come. He's proud of the part he's playing as a pioneer in the conquest of the universe.

Marjorie Slayton shares that pride. She loves to watch her husband handling a powerful jet, and she's looking forward to the vicarious thrill of knowing that he's in an orbiting satellite hundreds of miles above the Earth. She has never had an attack of nerves over her husband's trade. Once, at the Langley Air Force Base swimming pool, she was introduced as "the wife of one of the astronauts." The reaction she drew was a pitying one—but Marjorie finds herself puzzled and annoyed by the implication that she is married to a man soon to be a martyr to space. She takes the program in her stride, sees less drama in it than others do, and regards it all as just another and more complex testing assignment for her husband.

Wisconsin-born Slayton is described as a composed, serious man who tries hard not to appear sentimental. He keeps himself busy in making little household repairs, in playing with his young son, and with an array of hobbies that ranges from hunting, fishing and skiing through archery, riflery, and photography.

Carpenter, Cooper, Schirra, Slayton—this is the able second team that stands behind the prime trio of Glenn, Grissom, and Shepard. Other astronauts will be joining their number as the years go along, but these are the first seven. These are the men who will be making orbital flights around the Earth during the months that come. These are the men who will be first to the Moon.

These seven are America's pioneers of space.

Chapter Eight

THE MAKING OF AN ASTRONAUT

Few men have ever been asked to excel in so many departments of existence as the Mercury Astronauts. The NASA's requirements called for what were literally, supermen. And the feeling generally is that the seven men who emerged from the screening process were just that—supermen.

None of the seven can read minds, fly through the air unaided, deflect bullets, or perform any of the fantastic stunts of the comic-book heroes. What they have, the plus elements that put them into the superhuman class, can best be called a *general* superiority. They are better at more things than most men. Individual humans can run faster than any of the Mercury Astronauts. Others can thing faster than any of them. Still others have better reflexes. But few can match these seven in as *many* departments. On overall performance, they have to be rated as standouts.

And that was only the beginning. The seven men whose names were announced on April 9, 1959, were already exceptional human beings. But mere excellence was not enough. The seven Mercury Astronauts were scheduled to be transformed, by means of a rigorous training program, into super-supermen.

This is what the training of an astronaut is like.

In order to fit an astronaut properly for the experiences he would encounter during this orbital flight, training had to proceed on a number of fronts simultaneously. Initially, of course, the men had to be in prime physical condition— and to stay that way. Riding a capsule in orbit is itself not a strenuous job, but getting up there—and getting back—may call for unusual physical exertions. So, it goes without saying, the astronauts had to keep in shape.

But beyond that, special problems of space had to be mastered in advance. The problem of weightlessness, for one. The problem of eating while in orbit. The problem of enduring great heat. The problem of the psychological hurdles of facing the emptiness of space.

Aside from these special training programs, the astronauts had to go to school. The Mercury flight is primarily an observation attempt, and unless we send a trained observer up to report on what he is experiencing, we might as well be sending only chimpanzees. In order to report properly, the astronauts had to master the entire subject of space— to become versed in astronomy, meteorology, astronautics, geography, missile operation theory, and a host of other special disciplines. And—as engineers—they were called upon to work as full-fledged members of the team designing the capsule, taking a day-by-day part in the project. Being a Mercury Astronaut, then, was not simply a matter of waiting idly around for the day when word came to climb aboard. It was work, hard work. It was a full-time job for each of the seven men.

One of the first—and roughest—of the training procedures was carried out at the Naval Air Development Center in Johnsville, Pennsylvania. There, clad in flight suits and helmets, and seated in contour couches individually molded to fit their bodies, each astronaut in turn took a whirl in a 50-foot centrifuge designed to simulate space flight.

An accelerating rocket must fight a steady battle against the drag of gravity. A rocket that is not powerful enough will lose that battle and fall helplessly back to Earth. One that is too powerful will succeed in escaping from Earth's gravitational grip, but at the cost of shattering the fragile human within. At Johnsville, the astronauts were put through a simulated flight from take-off to re-entry, in an attempt to find out just how much they could take.

Acceleration is measured in G's—in units of the force of gravity. All of us, walking about on the surface of the Earth, are subject to a one-G pull. When we ride up in a fast-moving elevator, we feel pressed toward the floor— an example of an increase in G pull. An airplane climbing rapidly produces the same effect even more clearly. And, of course, an Atlas rocket heading upward at a speed of thousands of miles an hour will bring a great number of G's to bear on its encapsulated passenger. The astronauts had to be prepared for the sudden heavy fist of acceleration pressing down on them with a force that could double or triple or octuple their own weight almost instantaneously.

Research into the human ability to withstand G pull had been going on for half a dozen years before the selection of the Mercury Astronauts, and the work of other brave pioneers in centrifuges and aboard rocket sleds had shown that an acceleration as great as *forty-five* G's could be withstood briefly if the load were distributed properly over the body. Of course, high G existence is by no means comfortable—but it can be survived.

Strapped into the centrifuge, the Mercury Astronauts were whirled around violently, like helpless victims in the fun house at a carnival, to get a taste of life at high acceleration. On five-minute rides, they were whirled gradually up from one or two Gs to six, seven, eight Gs. Faces became drawn, features distorted. Speaking—through microphones connected to monitor speakers outside the centrifuge—became a strain. Eyeballs bulged as the centrifuge whirled faster and faster. A photo of Scott Carpenter undergoing a fourteen-G acceleration shows his face pulled weirdly out of shape. Other astronauts reported difficulties in moving or breathing as the acceleration approached the eyeball-bulging figure of twenty Gs. At a twenty-G acceleration, a 200-pound man has the sensation of weighing two *tons*.

No matter how many times a man is whirled through a centrifuge, it never becomes fun. As the acceleration mounts, eyelids droop, cheeks sag, lead weights seem to drag at your internal organs. Pain stabs at your chest. You feel as though a massive hand is gripping you, squeezing with ever growing power.

The Mercury Astronauts found the repeated drills in the Johnsville centrifuge nothing to look forward to—but they were necessary. And so, time after time, the seven astronauts took their places, one after another, in the giant centrifuge, bracing themselves against the sudden thrust. When they make their orbital flights, they may never experience the brutal twenty-G accelerations that they were sometimes put through at Johnsville—but at least now they have been prepared for the worst, and can withstand whatever comes with the knowledge that they have been through it all dozens of times before.

Not as bone-jarring as the centrifuge, but equally demanding on mind and body, was the test and training device know as MASTIF--short for Multiple Axis Space Test Inertia Facility. MASTIF, constructed at the NASA's Lewis Research Center in Cleveland, was designed to harden the astronauts to the wild three-way tumbles they might encounter while riding the capsule.

The problem MASTIF was aimed to cope with is called the "popgun effect." This would occur, at least in theory, at the moment when the manned capsule freed itself from its Atlas booster rocket. Just as a cork popping out of the muzzle of a toy gun will spin unpredictably in the air, because of the unevenness of the force propelling it out, so, too, could the Mercury capsule go into a wild tumbling motion when cutting loose. Three tiny rockets are to be used to effect the separation, and as they kick the capsule free from the Atlas it will be impossible to achieve fully even propulsion. Thus, a certain amount of tumbling will result.

Automatic control systems built into the capsule are supposed to cope with this problem. The autopilot will deal with the tumbling by firing stabilizing jets to control the motion. If the autopilot somehow does not deal with the tumbling as planned, the astronaut can take over operation of the capsule and fire the control jets himself. Further safeguards see to it that, if these jets are on the blink the pilot can switch on another automatic system to stabilize the tumbling capsule. And if *this* system is malfunctioning, too, a separate set of jets can be fired manually by the astronaut, either electrically or mechanically.

This multitude of control systems guarantees that even in the most widly unlikely series of mechanical malfunctions, the astronaut will still be able to regain control of his tumbling capsule—*provided* the weird gyrations don't interfere with his abilities to think and act in a crisis.

And hence MASTIF.

MASTIF is made up of three metal frameworks, one within the other. Innermost of all is a massive chair, much like a throne, similar in design to the chair in the actual Mercury capsule. The chair is mounted in such a way that it spins on its long axis. The next framework is a cage surrounding the chair and gimbaled to spin on its short axis. Outermost is a larger aluminum cage, designed to provide an end-over-end kind of motion. A cluster of tanks mounted in all the tubing holds nitrogen that is used to set the cages whirling and to stabilize them again.

The astronaut takes his seat at the heart of the maze of aluminum that is MASTIF.

"Try the innermost cage first," calls out one of the men supervising the test—perhaps Joe Algranti, an NASA test pilot who has trained intensively in MASTIF and who now aids the astronauts in their training, or Bob Miller, NASA project engineer. The astronaut nods his okay. At the control panel, Miller flips a switch. The nitrogen tanks emit gas blasts that set the chair spinning, up to thirty spins a minute. The astronaut is relaxed, untroubled, knowing the worst is still ahead.

The chair slows, Algranti speaks briefly to the astronaut on the interphone, and then the middlemost cage is activated. The astronaut begins to spin again, this time head over heels at thirty spins a minute. The first time, he was merely dizzied, but now the feeling is a sickening one. Once every two seconds his head and his feet change places. Within him, stomach and liver and intestines joggle mercilessly. He hangs on tight, gritting his teeth.

Again the cage is slowed, and finally the third axis is tested. Round and round the astronaut goes, like a ballet dancer whirling at blurring speed, until the figure of thirty rpms is reached.

"Okay," Algranti calls out. "Now for a little exercise. All three axes at once, this time."

What had gone before was just a warm-up. Now the astronaut will have to cope with roll, pitch and yaw, simultaneously. Here at Lewis Research Center, the worst that can happen to him is an upset stomach. But he knows that before long he'll be facing the same kind of conditions alone in a tumbling space capsule high above the Earth—

and Miller and Algranti won't be there to run the controls for him.

The astronaut draws in his breath expectantly and leans back against his couch of plastic foam. An instrument panel is two feet in front of him, and he studies the round dial in the middle. Three needles waver there, one indicating pitch, one indicating roll, one indicating yaw. His right hand closes on a control stick. By manipulating the stick the right way, he will be able to bring the madly gyrating MASTIF to a halt.

The swiveling frameworks pick up speed. The astronaut in the center is being tumbled in three directions at once. The quiet voice in his earphones keeps track of the mounting speed of revolutions: "Eight rpm . . . twelve . . . fifteen . . . how's it going in there?"

The astronaut has his eyes on the control dial. But as the whirling frameworks gain speed, the dial begins to blur, to disappear. The phenomenon know as "*vestibular nystagmus*" is setting in—a result of the violent shaking up that his body is enduring. His eyes will not focus. His balance mechanism is hopelessly awry.

But now MASTIF levels off at a constant 30 rpm along all three axes—the top limit of endurance for any of the astronauts. The man within the triple cages struggles to get control of his eyes as speed becomes constant. His head throbs, his stomach seems to be entangled with his windpipe, his liver and lungs feel as though they've changed places. In another moment or two, he knows he'll be violently and messily sick.

But—sweat beads spangling his forehead now—he forces himself to concentrate on the blurred dial. Somehow, despite the savage inexorability of the whirling cages, he overcomes the nystagmus and reads the dial translating the information of the triple needles into motions of his right hand on the control stick.

As he fires the stabilizing jets, the speed of MASTIF drops. But, as deceleration begins, the change of velocity affects his sense of balance once again, and the nystagmus returns. He pulls the control stick to neutral and waits for his eyeballs to settle down. Then he reads the dial again, fires the jets. Deceleration has to be managed in slow stages. Fire the jets, go to neutral, wait for the nystagmus to disappear. Fire the jets again. Wait. Fire. Wait. Little by little, the cage's mad whirling ceases. MASTIF slows to a halt. Wobbly-legged but gratified at his performance, the astronaut stumbles out and lets the next man take his place. He does not stay around to watch; MASTIF can be be just as unsettling from the observer's viewpoint as from the pilot's, and he has had enough for the time being.

The grueling ordeal of MASTIF was a regular part of the training of the Mercury Astronauts. The blurred vision and nausea they experienced became an unremarkable part of the routine. MASTIF training was of vital importance, however, because it not only acclimated the astronauts to the worst possible emergency conditions, but also gave them added confidence in their ability to handle the capsule. The project planners do not expect the actual capsule to tumble at anything approaching the 30 rpms of MASTIF—probably three or four rpms will be the worst to be encountered. But after a man has come safely out of a 30-rpm three-way tumble, he will have no fears of a spin only a tenth as violent.

Also, points out Astronaut Virgil Grissom, whose special area of responsibility embraces the manual-control operation, the confidence supplied by MASTIF will enable the capsule's pilot to handle non-emergency situations with ease. He'll be able to fire his jets, turn the capsule over for a look at the stars, for a view of Earth, for a glimpse of the Moon. Knowing that he can handle himself under extreme circumstances, he'll have no inhibitions about imparting a little spin to the capsule for the sake of making better observations up there. For men who have all been pilots for years, this feeling of direct control over the capsule is psychologically healthy and will lead to better experimental results during the orbiting flights.

Another unique space condition that must be anticipated and trained for on the ground is weightlessness. This is the opposite extreme from the condition of high-G acceleration for which the centrifuge training is used. During the powered ascent of a rocket—or during the climb of an elevator, for that matter—acceleration builds up, in the form of high-G. But when the engine of a rocket is cut off—or when an elevator cable snaps and the elevator plummets down its shaft—those within experience total or near-total weightlessness. There is no sense of a gravitational pull. Anything not fastened down floats free.

Since it is hardly practical to make observations in plummeting elevators, there was little knowledge of the actual physical and physiological effects of weightlessness when our space program started. Some medical men felt that the effects might be severe. They suggested damage to the heart and lungs as definite possibilities, along with a general loss of sensory co-ordination that might destroy a spaceman's sanity.

Human reactions under conditions of weightlessness had to be tested—and the astronauts had to be prepared for the several hours of weightlessness they would endure while in orbit. The only human experience with true weightlessness had been fragmentary; a diver, a parachutist, a jumper, all have a weightless sensation, but only for seconds at a time —not long enough to draw conclusions from.

The development of high-speed jets and rocket planes made possible the experience of zero gravity for longer periods of time—up to a minute or more. A jet diving in a roller-coaster arc at supersonic speeds does provide fifty or sixty seconds of total weightlessness. Using T-33A and F-94C jets, Air Force researchers were able to study zero-G intensively as early as six years ago. By 1958, one pilot alone had logged over thirty hours of weightlessness, in stretches of less than a minute at a time, and had reported no ill effects.

Said USAF test pilot Major Charles E. Yeager, a pioneer in this kind of work, "When getting to a point of pulling zero gravity, it feels as though the blood pressure is increasing. You get a swelling of the head . . . But after two or three experiences of about 25-30 seconds of zero gravity, I don't see any reason why a man cannot change his habits so that he counteracts and compensates. But so far as physical effects of extended periods of time of weightlessness are concerned, I don't know, and I don't think any-one does, because there have been no experiences and there won't be any experience along that line until we have zero gravity that will extend into possibly hours or days."

There is no way to simulate zero-G conditions on Earth except for the 60-second stretches on arcing jets. Therefore, the Mercury Astronauts will be the first Americans to ex-perience *sustained* weightlessness. This is the big question mark of the program, since it cannot be tested in advance. The best that can be done is to give the men brief tastes of zero-G, watch for danger signs, and guess.

The two-seater F-100F jet was used for the zero-G train-ing flights. All of the astronauts had experienced fleeting moments of weightlessness during their test-pilot careers, but none had gone about making a serious trial of zero-G conditions until the test period at Edwards Air Force Base in California.

Each man took the F-100F up on a series of flights, climbing to 40,000 feet and reaching the speed of 600 mph. Under full power, they dived at a 30-degree angle, reaching 900 mph by the time they were at 25,000 feet. Then, pulling out of the dive, they roared upward again at 55 degrees, cutting the engine off at the top of the climb. This time, unpowered, the jet would curve downward in a long weight-less descent, with the pilot finally pulling out and restoring power.

The entire maneuver—known as a "parabolic flight"—not only affords nearly a minute of weightlessness, but pro-vides high-G acceleration during the pull-out, so the pilot experiences the actual sequence of a rocket flight—accelera-tion of several Gs, followed by zero-G, followed by accelera-tion again.

To provide a running check on whether or not weightless-ness was actually being achieved, an orange golf ball was suspended by a length of nylon string from the top of the cockpit canopy. So long as the golf ball floated loosely in midair, zero-G was being attained. But if the nylon string pulled taut, or if the ball swung from side to side the way it would if similarly suspended on Earth, it meant that the pilot wasn't successfully handling the weightlessness maneuver. The ball drifting lazily in front of the pilot's face provided the best indication of the lack of gravitational pull during the flight.

During the flights, the astronauts were tested in various ways. On some flights they had to work an electrical panel that measured the speed and accuracy of their responses. On others, they practiced eating and drinking weightless food. On other flights, they had the job of handling the controls while their comrades went through the other tests.

The efficiency test involved orange lights that would wink on from time to time. A red button had to be pushed to put each light out as soon as it went on. The astronauts reported difficulties only during the moments of transition into and out of zero-G. A sudden shift from a 3-G acceleration to weightlessness resulted in overshooting the buttons on the first attempt, while the return of gravity dragged hands away from the panel. However, once the astronauts adjusted to the situation, they were able to make compensations that permitted a co-ordinated response at all times.

Eating and drinking were accomplished by using plastic squeeze-bottles. Under weightlessness, knife-and-fork eating is impossible—peas, for instance, would simply float off the plate—and the squeeze-bottle technique is the only feasible eating method. The astronauts managed it without difficulty, though they were far from delighted with the cuisine—beef and fruit pureed to mush, as in baby foods.

Some of the astronauts indulged in mischief during these test, as when Virgil Grissom held his squeeze bottle of orange juice up and squeezed out a few drops of juice, which went floating around the cabin like small orange balloons. During their orbital flight, the astronauts will have to subsist on this sort of liquified pap for lack of any other way of serving food under zero-G conditions.

The astronauts were wired for medical observation during their brief zero-G flights. Telemetered data on pulse rate, breathing, and blood pressure was transmitted to medics on the ground. No significant physical disturbance was noticed during zero-G flight. After each flight, psychological tests were administered to learn how the astronauts had reacted mentally to the feeling of being cut off from all gravity. Their reactions to weightlessness ranged from indifference to delight, but none of the men found the experience at all unpleasant.

But reactions to longer periods of weightlessness must remain untested until the first orbital flight. A program of skin-diving gives the astronauts a rough approximation of what extended weightlessness will be like, and frequent jet flights add to the growing fund of information. But some experiments indicate that prolonged weightlessness over a period of days may have definite harmful effects.

A recent test involving a doctor at the Air Force School of Aviation Medicine showed this: the doctor equipped himself in a rubber skin-diving suit, mounted a floating beach chair, and spent seven days in a tank of water, only his head above the surface. The effect was one of weightlessness for a week. At the end of the test, the doctor discovered that his muscles had softened, his circulation was bad, and even his bones appeared to have lost strength. In addition, his mental reactions were blurred and hazy.

The problems of extended weightlessness will have to be faced, not by the Mercury Astronauts (who will be weightless only a few hours) but by the next generation of spacemen. But despite the positive results of the 60-second zero-G tests in the F-100F, the problem of weightlessness remains the major uncertainty for the men in orbit.

Other aspects of the astronauts' training concentrated on preparing them for the various stages of their flight. For example, one routine that had to be practiced constantly was that of escape from the capsule after it has returned from orbit. The capsule will land in a rough sea, and the impact of landing may shatter the watertight walls. Unless he is to drown in his own capsule, the astronaut will have to be able to make a quick exit.

Escape techniques were drilled constantly in a pool at Langley Research Center, where a special machine simulated rough ocean conditions. The astronauts practiced releasing the harness tying them to the couch within the capsule, loosening the ventilator hose which has been supplying their pressure suits with cool air, and uncoupling a section of the instrument panel to squeeze out of the capsule. A sealed pressure hatch behind the instrument panel must be opened.

The canister that held the capsule's landing parachutes must be unfastened and pushed to one side. The inflatable life raft and survival kit must be shoved through the opening, after which the astronaut himself crawls out.

The escape procedure calls for agility, strength, and co-ordination. The astronauts rehearsed over and over again the delicate maneuver of emerging from the capsule without tipping it, of inflating the raft, of protecting the survival kit. Once safely in his raft, the astronaut can broadcast an SOS over a small battery-operated radio. He will be carrying a signal mirror, smoke flares, and pellets of dye, all to be used to attract rescuers. If all of these fail, he must prepare to drift in his raft, following standard castaway survival procedures until picked up.

After training in the pool at Langley under the simulated conditions ranging from complete calm to eight-foot waves, the astronauts went to the Gulf of Mexico for further training under actual ocean circumstances. With Navy skin-divers standing by in case of emergency, the astronauts, burdened by their cumbersome aluminized pressure suits, practiced clambering out of their capsules, inflating their rafts, and making use of their rescue devices.

The survival training course was rugged; getting out of the narrow-necked capsule in a choppy sea is a job only for a man in the peak of physical condition. Even a tough Marine like John Glenn nearly became seasick after gulping down mouthfuls of salt water in repeated escape maneuvers. And, a day after Glenn's misadventure, Astronauts Slayton and Carpenter—along with Glenn, once again—ran into heavy going after they had boarded their life rafts. A helicopter was sent out to rescue them, but the astronauts insisted on riding out the wind, only to find themselves tossed roughly up on a nearby island.

Another survival technique the astronauts practiced was use of the emergency escape: an explosive escape hatch located next to the astronaut's couch. The explosive exit will get them out of the capsule in a hurry, but the capsule will be destroyed in the process; it will be employed only as a last resort, since it is considered desirable to save the capsule when possible. The rugged process of exiting from a capsule in a choppy sea involved the astronauts in a training program that was not so exotic as MASTIF, but far more strenuous.

In many other ways, the astronauts were prepared physically and mentally for the job ahead of them. One of the exercises designed to improve dexterity made use of a revolving room at the Navy School of Aviation Medicine at Pensacola, Florida. Seated inside the room, which was revolving at 10 times a minute, each astronaut was asked to toss tennis balls into a wastebasket. The simple exercise contributed to their co-ordination and poise under motion situations, and will aid them when the time comes to manipulate controls in a moving space capsule.

To guard against the danger of a desert landing after re-entry, the astronauts learned how to fashion tents from their parachutes, stretching them out over their life rafts to shield them from the sun. They practiced cutting Arab-style burnooses from their parachute cloth, as survival aids in the desert. The possibility of a miscalculated landing that would drop the capsule on land instead of in the ocean had to be taken into account.

The Mercury team spent several days in the desert near Fallon, Nevada, brushing up on its landside survival techniques in 110-degree heat. Under conditions that could kill an unsheltered man in two days if he were deprived of water, the astronauts tested the limits of their endurance.

Astronaut John Glenn, interested in studying the effects of dehydration, purposely avoided any water intake for several hours. He rapidly became so weak he could barely lift and use his signal mirror. When he finally permitted himself to quench his thirst, he drank fifteen pints of water in a matter of hours—and still felt thirsty.

Supplementing MASTIF and the Johnsville centrifuge is a training device known at the Flight Procedures Trainer. This is a dummy capsule whose control systems are connected to monitoring pickups and computers. The Flight Procedures Trainer can provide a simulation of any conceivable routine or unusual performance by the capsule, thus permitting the astronauts to rehearse any eventuality.

After some months of regular use of the trainer, the astronauts were able to react on the level of conditioned reflex to any danger situation thrown at them by the machine. One of the Flight Procedures Trainers has been set up at the Mercury Control Center at Cape Canaveral, where the men who will be monitoring the actual orbital flight have been able to gain familiarity with the operation of the capsule while the astronauts train inside it.

Learning to use the special pressure suit that they will wear in the capsule was another important part of the astronauts' training. The pressure suits—which cost $3,750 apiece—were tailored to the astronauts' precise measurements with great care. Each astronaut, clad in long underwear, was encased completely in wet strips of paper tape. When the tape had dried, it and the underwear was cut away, to be used as the molds from which the B.F. Goodrich Company prepared the actual suits.

The suits are complex. The inner layer is rubber, the outer layer aluminized nylon. Originally, an extra layer of sponge rubber was included to protect the astronauts against the heat of re-entry, but this layer was eliminated when preliminary capsule tests showed that the heat problem would not be as great as anticipated earlier.

The suit is the astronaut's final wall against the vacuum of space. It will be worn continuously during the orbiting trip, but will be sealed and inflated only in emergency. Should the capsule spring a leak and air pressure start to fall, electronic sensor devices will notify the astronaut. He then must quickly close his helmet's face plate. The suit will automatically inflate, providing a completely self-contained environment.

Maneuvering inside an inflated pressure suit was no easy matter, the astronauts discovered early in their training program. At full pressure of five pounds per square inch, the suit takes on inflexible rigidity. Even the smallest movement calls for special effort. Since a suit-encased astronaut may be called upon to perform complicated and small-scale operations, long hours of practice were called for—as well as occasional modifications in the suit itself to allow for greater freedom of action.

And, once fitted for a suit, an astronaut must be careful not to let his weight rise radically; a new fitting would be required if an astronaut gained as much as five pounds. But with the rigors of the astronaut training program to contend with, most of the men had no problem keeping their weights down.

Environmental preparation has played an important role in training also. The seven astronauts have spent hours in soundproof isolation chambers, accustoming themselves to the silent black emptiness of space. They have sweltered in steam chambers, testing their tolerance to the great heat they may encounter on their descents through the atmosphere. They have spent time in pressure chambers.

The astronaut training program is not merely tough physically, though. The men have been through tough postgraduate courses in a dozen branches of science and technology. To enable them to pinpoint physical reactions in flight—and so they will not be hampered by lack of knowledge when something seems to be going wrong with their bodies—the Mercury Astronauts have been given intensive training in physiology. They are familiar with the workings of their body, and will understand the mechanics of their reactions to high acceleration, weightlessness, pressure, and other space conditions. As trained observers, they will be able to give first-hand accounts of what it is like to ride in the Mercury capsule.

Math, physics, geography, astronautics—all these have gone to make up the curriculum for the seven Mercury men. They have emerged from their training as far beyond their 1958 selves at those 1958 selves were beyond the ordinary run of human being. Expert now in every phase of space research, skilled in half a dozen specialized disciplines, and physically toughened by a constant program of exertion and hardening, they have transformed themselves into men of almost frightening capability.

Perhaps no other men in history have ever been honed to a keener edge. They are, in the truest sense of the word, *supermen*. They have gone through the crucible of an astronaut's training and have emerged, their few weaknesses burned away, ready and willing for the challenge of the void that awaits them.

Chapter Nine

THE SPACE CAPSULE

The three-year training program of the Mercury Astronauts has brought the seven men to a peak of capability. But the human factor is only part of Project Mercury. For all their talents, co-ordination and intelligence, the astronauts still are only passengers. They are dependent on the smooth functioning of their rocket booster and of the capsule in which they will ride.

The space capsule itself is the core of the project. Its manufacturer, the McDonnell Aircraft Corporation, developed it within weeks after the announcement of the project in late 1958, but has been busily perfecting and refining it ever since.

The capsule is shaped more or less like a huge television tube, blunt at one end, tapering rapidly. The astronaut sits with his back to the blunt face, with a heat shield behind him. The heat shield bears a coating of resinous glass fiber which will vaporize in the heat and friction of re-entry, carrying away the heat with it. This is the process known as *ablation*, first developed to protect the nose cones of ballistic missiles during their re-entry to the atmosphere.

The astronaut will feel little of the 2600-degree heat assailing the heat shield. He will be within a double-walled hull, well insulated against the fierce heat outside. The capsule has been designed so that cabin heat should never rise above 120 degrees—uncomfortable enough, but not fatal—regardless of external conditions.

Within the capsule, strapped in his throne-like couch, the astronaut faces an instrument panel. Behind him, sprouting from the blunt heat shield, are the retro-rockets that will blast him loose from his giant Atlas booster rocket. (It is at this point that the tumbling phenomenon prepared for in MASTIF is likely to occur.) The retro-rockets will be used again to establish the capsule in its planned orbit, and then will be jettisoned.

In the narrow end of the capsule, the end toward which the astronaut will face, are located the main parachute, the small braking chute, and the exit hatch. At the very end of the narrow part of the capsule is the "spoiler," a hinged metal flap to be used as a mechanical stabilizer in landing emergencies. The capsule is supposed to return to the atmosphere blunt end foremost, to get the benefit of the heat shielding. In the event that the capsule is coming in wrong end around, and if the stabilizing control jets are not functioning properly, the "spoiler" can be opened out, digging into the air blast and causing the capsule to flip into the proper position for descent.

One of the most ingenious gadgets devised for the capsule's instrument panel is a revolving globe that bears markings for longitude, latitude, topography, and major cities. Watching this globe through a window in his instrument panel, the astronaut will be able to follow his position just as though he were looking down on Earth itself. A bull's-eye sight on the window allows him to find his own position relative to ground points, while other guide markings tell him where he would land if he fired the return rockets at that particular moment. An observation port viewed through a periscope will also give him a direct view of the universe outside his capsule.

With its outer shell of heat-resistant cobalt and its inner shell of titanium, the capsule comprises a self-inclosed world. The astronaut will experience none of the heat or cold of the various stages of his trip, none of the noise.

The atmosphere of the capsule is to be pure oxygen. Before launching, the capsule cabin will be pumped free of air, then filled with oxygen. Oxygen's pressure of five pounds per square inch—a third that of air at sea level—will give the astronaut an environment similar in pressure to that encountered at 27,000-foot altitudes—say, the height of Mount Everest.

But the chilling cold of the Himalayas will not be present inside the capsule, and the astronaut, superb physical specimen that he must be, will have no difficulties breathing the thin atmosphere. He may choose to leave his face mask open and breathe the capsule cabin's atmosphere, or else seal his mask and breathe the similar oxygen atmosphere of his suit's recirculating system. To do the latter is safer, but it will be far more comfortable to leave the helmets open. In case of a leak—the result of a meteorite puncture, perhaps —the astronaut whose helmet is open will be able to live only ten to twelve seconds without oxygen. He will have to seal his face mask rapidly in order to survive the sudden penetration of the capsule's hull. And, on the re-entry, he will need to keep his visor closed, for protection against the heat.

The heat of descent has been a major engineering concern. Despite the outer heat of 2600 degrees or more, the inner wall of the cabin is not expected to grow hotter than about 200 degrees. The temperature of the cabin's atmosphere should not be much above 100 at any time during re-entry, provided the capsule's cooling system holds up. The astronauts have all experienced higher temperatures than that in heat chambers during their training. Once the descending capsule has reached 20,000 feet, a snorkel tube in the capsule's narrow end will admit fresh air from outside, to aid further in cooling the cabin.

At the outset of the orbital attempt, there will be a safety feature designed to free capsule and astronaut from a malfunctioning rocket. This will consist of an escape rocket, looking very much like an oversize firecracker, that will perch atop the narrow end of the capsule. At the first sign of a mishap on blastoff, this escape rocket will ignite and take the capsule safely free of its exploding booster. A parachute will then carry the capsule back to Earth. If the escape rocket is not needed, it will be jettisoned by the capsule shortly after the capsule's own separation from its booster rocket.

Every aspect of the Mercury capsule has undergone the most careful of testing before the life of even a monkey was risked in flight. The problem of heat-shielding came under study at the NASA's Ames Research Center near Palo Alto, California, where research in ablation—cooling through vaporization of the outer skin of the heat shield—

was carried on. Using models fashioned from frozen motor oil, Ames scientists made wind-tunnel tests, recording the ablation process photographically. In other tests, tiny plastic nose cones were fired from gas guns in an altitude chamber. At 12,000 miles an hour, the nose cones were white-hot before they reached the end of the tunnel. Months of this painstaking testing work preceded every step in the development of the capsule's heat shield.

The capsule has been tested repeatedly in unmanned flights. Some of these were unqualified successes; others resulted in unexpected failures, and sent the Mercury engineers back to the drawing boards to assess their miscalculations and eliminate the difficulty.

One such mishap occurred in November, 1960, during a test of the mechanism which is designed to separate the capsule from the booster rocket in case of emergency. The separation did not occur; capsule and booster fell back together into the ocean. It meant trouble and delay while the difficulty was isolated and dealt with for the next shot.

Another test-firing a few weeks later was even more of a fiasco. The countdown reached zero, the Redstone booster rocket began to rise—and then stopped abruptly and dropped back to the launching pad. Within seconds, the capsule's escape rocket fired itself, parachutes began to fly open in all directions, and the general atmosphere, amid the smoke and flame, was that of a holiday fireworks display running wild.

The engineers had some busy sessions after that particular failure. The discovery was ultimately made that a premature disconnection had shut the booster rocket's engines off in the first seconds after launching. The capsule control section had received the electronic signal it would normally receive when the booster engine cuts off in space. The escape rocket was fired because the capsule "thought" it would no longer be needed. But the parachutes opened because other control devices reported that the capsule was still surrounded by air, and thus in need of parachute stabilization. Once the parachutes opened, an automatic rescue operation was touched off by the capsule, which began to send out radio signals and flashing lights as it would during a normal descent from space. And all this was taking place while neither capsule nor booster left the launching pad! The confusion was comic and disheartening all at once—but, like every rocket-firing failure, it provided important information on what not to do the next time.

A third testing failure took place as recently as March 18, 1961, resulting in the postponement of the first ballistic manned shot, which otherwise would have taken place several weeks later. This was a test at Wallops Island, Virginia, where the NASA maintains its own rocket-launching facilities. A Little Joe rocket bearing a Mercury capsule was fired, and the capsule separated on schedule from its booster at 35,000 feet, continuing to 40,000 feet on its own momentum before beginning to descend.

At 10,000 feet, the capsule's parachutes opened. But a number of minor flaws marred the shot. The capsule landed twenty miles out at sea, instead of the planned distance of six miles. Project director Robert Gilruth cited "some irregularity in the firing sequence," although the altitude and course of the rocket were satisfactory. The escape rocket had gone off after thirty-five seconds, somewhat earlier than scheduled.

Other discouraging features were the facts that both parachutes had opened instead of just one, causing the capsule to drift out to sea—one of the chutes was supposed to remain folded as a reserve—and that the parachutes had failed to disengage from the capsule when it hit the water. Because of this, the capsule could not be picked up by a helicopter, and had to be towed in by a tub. Also, the capsule was badly dented, indicating that it had hit either the booster rocket or the escape tower to which the escape rocket is attached.

This melange of unexpected minor hitches depressed the Mercury designers—but the test program had been developed just so these things would be encountered and dealt with *before* one of the astronauts went up.

An even more violent malfunction had taken place in July, 1960. A capsule and its Atlas booster exploded after rising to an altitude of 40,000 feet. The capsule was completely demolished, and its fragments, found in the ocean, were painstakingly reassembled by technicians in an attempt to study the causes of the explosion.

But these failures in the test program have been the exceptions. By and large, the project has moved along even faster than most had expected.

The first successful test of the capsule took place as far back as September 9, 1959. This test was designed to check on the heat-resistant capabilities of the capsule. An Atlas rocket was used as the booster in the Cape Canaveral firing, and the capsule was recovered in the South Atlantic. Although the capsule did not attain its planned flight distance, the steeper re-entry angle that resulted put it through an even sterner heat test than had been called for. The capsule came safely through a heat that reached 10,000 degrees Fahrenheit, to the great delight of its designers and of the men who ultimately would have to ride it.

Then, on December 4, 1959, the escape mechanism system was tested at Wallops Island, this time with a live "astronaut" on board, the rhesus monkey, Sam, as discussed in an earlier chapter. Sam and his space capsule were safely recovered from the Atlantic, suffering no ill effects. The experiment was repeated a few weeks later with another rhesus monkey, *Miss* Sam, in the capsule. On other tests, the capsule alone was launched atop Atlas or Redstone rockets, and recovered successfully.

A fair imitation of an actual manned ballistic flight took place on January 31, 1961. A male chimpanzee nicknamed "Ham," who tipped the scales at a whopping thirty-seven pounds, took a 420-mile ride through space in a Mercury capsule. Ham was the heaviest experimental animal to have been shot into space up to that time, either by the United States or Russia. The Russian space-dogs are thought to have weighed no more than twelve to fifteen pounds apiece.

Ham's history-making Mercury ballistic flight began at Cape Canaveral, Florida, at 11:55 in the morning on the 31st. The three-year-eight-month-old chimp had been given a thorough physical the night before, and at 7:15 in the morning of his big day he was fed some cooking oil, half a fresh egg, an ounce of baby cereal, four ounces of condensed milk, and a quarter of a package of gelatin. Then he was strapped into the specially designed, chimp-sized contour couch aboard the space capsule. His arms were left free. His capsule's environmental control system was the same as that planned for the human astronauts; he breathed the same atmosphere, at the same low pressure, and was subjected to the same stresses.

Ham had been specially trained to perform mechanical operations during his space flight. A system of three lights and three levers was rigged above his couch. A red light was set to burn continuously; a white light flashed when the correct lever was pushed; a blue light shone for five-second bursts every two minutes. The system was designed so that Ham would get a mild shock every twenty seconds unless he pushed the lever under the white bulb, and every two minutes unless he pushed the lever under the blue bulb. Apparently he went through his complicated little game with complete nonchalance during the flight.

With as much solemnity as though a Mercury Astronaut were being launched and not merely a grinning young chimp, the Canaveral men sent Ham's rocket aloft. It climbed steeply, then headed down the Atlantic missile range. A recovery fleet of eight naval vessels was waiting near the target area, 290 miles from Canaveral, but the rocket overshot by 130 miles. The capsule dropped into the sea in the Caribbean off the Bahamas. The recovery ship headed for the site, and a helicopter sent out by the U.S.S. *Donner* plucked the capsule from the sea at 2:52 P.M., just short of three hours after blastoff. (The ride through space had lasted eighteen minutes.)

There was some fear for Ham's life, because of the overshooting and because the re-entry had been rougher than anticipated, exposing the chimp to a force of sixteen Gs instead of the intended eleven Gs. Half an hour after pickup, the capsule was opened aboard the *Donner,* and Ham's voice could be heard. He sounded a little troubled. An oxygen hose was inserted through the hatch and, shortly after, the capsule was opened and Ham removed.

Major Richard Benson, an Air Force veterinarian, gave the chimp a physical check-up and pronounced him "healthy and happy." The only signs of his trip through space were a bump on his nose and a slight wobbliness of the legs, ascribed to fatigue and a fourteen-hour fast. The wobbliness cleared up rapidly when Ham got his first meal after returning from space—an apple.

Despite the sprightliness of the space chimp, the test was not a complete success, even though a Mercury Astronaut would almost certainly have survived it. The 130-mile overshoot, caused by a faulty fuel-consumption rate in the Redstone booster, was a cause for distress. And a small valve had failed to close in the capsule, admitting a foot and a half of water before the rescuers reached Ham. An Astronaut, of course, could have freed himself from a leaking capsule, but the mechanical failure even of a small valve was a worrisome thing. The rocket had also taken Ham to a height of 155 miles, forty more than expected, and the space capsule had lost its heat shield in the water upon landing.

The net combination of unplanned miscues meant that more testing would be needed before one of the seven astronauts was risked in an attempt to duplicate Ham's flight. But, proving that a large animal could make a ballistic ride in a Mercury capsule, maintain physical coordination throughout, and emerge in good spirits, the attempt was considered a major success in the space program.

Before Ham's flight atop a Redstone missile, painstaking testing had established the safety of the shot. Time after time, the capsule had been checked out in static tests—mounted to a Redstone whose engines fire but without leaving the ground—to see the effects of vibration and noise on the capsule's interior. The complex electronic control mechanisms of the Redstone had been quadruple-checked through a testing program of formidable care.

The capsule itself had been through a fierce barrage of tests ever since the first scale models were prepared. A splash test involved the dropping of larger and larger models of the capsule into a tank of water, always at the 54-degree angle anticipated for the final flight. Larger and larger models were used, testing the stress of the 30-feet-per-second impact. The capsule stood up.

Heat tests involved air jets of greater than 5000 degrees Fahrenheit applied to plastic and fiberglass models. In other tests, the capsules were pounded, dropped, beaten, roasted, and otherwise tormented to make sure they would remain spaceworthy under the most violent of conditions.

Encapsuled pigs were dropped to the ground ten times as hard as human astronauts will have to land. The pigs emerged unharmed.

Fire and water and wind have given the Mercury capsule its baptism. Rhesus monkeys and a freckle-faced chimpanzee have ridden in it. Thousands of experiments have been carried out to test the capsule design. Hundreds of parachute drops alone, from varying altitudes, have been made to ascertain the performance reliability of the 63-foot nylon canopy that will break the capsule's fall.

And now a man has made a ballistic ride through space. All that remains to do now is to achieve the orbital flight, the weightless trip around the world.

This is the space capsule. Six feet in diameter, ten feet high, weighing only a ton, it is hardly big enough to hold the man for whom it was designed. It has been engineered to the limits of perfection.

Sometime in the not very distant future, the Mercury capsule will be mounted at the snout of a big Atlas rocket. In a fury of smoke and sound, the Atlas will rise skyward, the capsule will separate, an orbit will be achieved. For the first time, an American will be totally cut off from the gravitational pull of Earth, riding in weightless splendor through the endless night of space. This will be the culmination of Project Mercury—and the signal for the next stage in the conquest of space.

Chapter Ten

THE FINAL COUNTDOWN

In the previous chapter, the center of interest was the capsule in which the astronauts ride. Now, we turn the focus on the booster, the rocket that supplies the push which will put our men into space.

Two different rockets have figured in Project Mercury, and it's important to keep their names and their roles entirely separate. The *Redstone* is the rocket used to put the chimpanzee, Ham, into space, and to provide the boost for the first manned ballistic flight that has just been successfully accomplished. The *Atlas* is the rocket that will be used, at the satisfactory completion of the ballistic tests, to put a spaceman and his capsule into orbit around the Earth.

The Redstone is one of the real veterans of our missile family, a tried-and-true rocket that has been fully operational since 1956. Developed at the U.S. Army Arsenal in Huntsville, Alabama, it is a direct descendant of the German V-2. The head of the Redstone designing team was Dr. Wernher von Braun, spearhead of the V-2 program in wartime Germany. Von Braun's V-2 team became the nucleus of our Guided Missile Laboratory at the Redstone Arsenal, which has been in the forefront of much of our missile work. It was the Redstone that was originally proposed by von Braun as the booster rocket for the ill-fated Project Orbiter in 1954.

True to its ancestry, the Redstone was designed primarily as a military weapon, a ballistic missile which climbs to a prescribed height, then arcs over and continues in a straight line to its target. As the booster section exhausts its fuel, it separates and drops away, while jets in the warhead section deliver the nuclear bomb. Von Braun proposed to modify the Redstone to make it suitable for lifting its payload into orbit instead of delivering it to a target. But the Orbiter idea became sidetracked when Project Vanguard gained Presidential approval.

Then, after the Vanguard fiasco of December, 1957, the Orbiter idea was hastily revived. This time, using the Redstone as the first stage of a composite rocket known as the Jupiter-C, von Braun's team succeeded in putting an Explorer satellite into orbit—our first.

The Redstone has a range of some 250 miles, though it has exceeded this on occasion—most notably (and unwantedly) when the rocket bearing the chimp, Ham, overshot its 290-mile range by 130 miles. It is 69 feet long, has a diameter of just under six feet (fourteen feet six inches across the fins) and weighs 62,000 pounds fully fueled for take-off. The rocket delivers a thrust of 78,000 pounds. It is much bigger than its ancestor, Germany's V-2, but has a number of similar features. It uses the same fuel, ethyl alcohol and liquid oxygen; it has turbine-driven centrifugal fuel pumps powered by the breakdown of hydrogen peroxide; its exhaust vanes are similarly constructed. The prime contractor responsible for building Redstones is the Chrysler Corporation.

The Redstone was chosen for the ballistic manned firings because of its proven reliability over a seven-year lifetime. Its range and power are limited—it could not lift the one-ton Mercury capsule into orbit, though it could orbit smaller satellites—but it is perfectly suited for the brief ballistic flights, which last less than twenty minutes and call for altitudes of no more than a hundred miles and firing ranges of two hundred to two-fifty. At the Huntsville, Alabama plants where Redstone missiles are turned out, those built for Project Mercury received special care in construction, with every component stamped with a symbol of the Roman god Mercury as a warning to the workmen that no defects could be permitted.

For the orbital flight, however, a more powerful rocket booster was called for. Again, a rocket designed primarily for military purposes was chosen: the powerful Atlas Intercontinental Ballistic Missile, which is the most reliable of our growing family of long-range missiles.

The Atlas, like the Redstone, is a liquid-fuel missile, which means a complex system of tubes and controls is necessary to power it—unlike such later, solid-fuel missiles as the Minuteman, whose firing system is far simpler and thus needs less of a countdown before blastoff. Developed by the Air Force, and built by the Convair Division of the General Dynamics Corporation, the Atlas has an over-all length of 82.5 feet, a diameter of ten feet, and a weight of 255,000 pounds at firing time—all of these figures exclusive of the additional burden of the Mercury capsule. It can be seen that though it is only thirteen feet taller than the Redstone, its weight is four times as great—and it delivers a thrust of 300,00 pounds in the first stage, 60,000 in the second stage, making it better than four times as powerful.

The Atlas is fueled with liquid oxygen and kerosene. Its range is 5000 to 9000 miles, most far-reaching of our present missiles. Early in its career, the Atlas had run into difficulties getting started; at the time of the first Sputnik launching in October, 1957, the United States had launched only two Atlas missiles, and both of these had exploded only a few thousand feet off the ground, despite an intensive Air Force development program dating back to 1951.

But the third Atlas firing, in December, 1957, was considered successful over its limited range. A series of progressively longer and more accurate shots in 1958 culminated in the Atlas test of November 28, 1958, when an Atlas homed in exactly on a target 6,235 miles from Cape Canaveral. And another Atlas triumph came three weeks later when a complete Atlas was placed in orbit to broadcast President Eisenhower's Christmas message.

During 1959, however, the Atlas program ran into a series of snags, with several consecutive failures setting the operation back. But by the summer of that year, four successful launchings in a row brought the Atlas to a fully operational status. In 1960 the Atlas added to its growing list of achievements when, on May 20, the 51st Atlas to be tested covered a prescribed course of 9000 miles in 55 minutes, landing in the Indian ocean. In August another Atlas climbed to a height of 1000 miles, far beyond its normal range, while traveling 7000 miles down the Atlantic testing area. And in September another 9000-mile flight was carried off without a hitch.

Atlas is actually the general term for an entire family of rockets. The one that will carry the astronuats into orbit is known as the Atlas-Mercury, Atlas-D. Other members of the family, designed for different tasks, include the Atlas-Agena A, the Atlas-Agena B, the Atlas-Centaur, and the Atlas-Able. These various rockets have the same basic first stage, but differ in the second and third stages.

The Atlas-Mercury has had a particularly intensive testing program, since it is the only one of the group intended to carry human beings in the immediate future. It posted sixteen successive perfect flights in 1959 and early 1960, but any overconfidence that might have resulted was rudely checked at the July 29, 1960 test, when the Atlas-Mercury exploded after only 65 seconds of flight. Further testing has gone on at Cape Canaveral under the direction of Convair engineer B.G. McNabb, and confidence in the Atlas-Mercury's capabilities is once again growing. As of the spring of 1961, the NASA felt that it would be safe to try a manned Atlas-Mercury orbital shot, perhaps by the end of 1961, or early 1962. In the meanwhile, repeated ballistic firings with the Redstone used as a booster would serve as warm-up training flights for the astronauts.

The time is drawing near, then, for that first orbital shot. Possibly it will take place a month after you read this, or maybe three months—or, perhaps, not for a year. Quite possibly all seven of the Mercury Astronauts will have had at least one opportunity apiece to ride their capsule through space with a Redstone booster. The NASA will have seen each man in action, will have found out how he reacts to the unforeseen stresses of that ballistic shot. With this evidence in hand, the choice will be made. One of the seven will be named. Word will go out to the men intimately involved with the project that a shot is imminent.

What will it be like, on the day of the first orbital shot? Let's try to picture the scene as it will unroll, a month or three months or a year hence.

We are at Cape Canaveral, Florida, the nation's space-launching center. It is still before dawn, and gray wisps of fog drift through the air. Out on the launching pad, an Atlas-D stands in silent majesty, jutting eighty-odd feet into the air, and topped by the tapering Mercury capsule and its escape-rocket tower. During the night, technicians have worked feverishly, checking out the thousands of separate parts that make up the big rocket. They have been told nothing about the shot that is to be made this morning. Officially, it is just another test flight, perhaps with a chimpanzee on board in the capsule. All during the year, flights of this sort have been made. But a rumor has been circulating since the early hours of the night. "This is going to be the big one!" they whisper to each other as they work.

The night before, the choice of an astronaut has been made. All seven know of the decision. They have come down from their Virginia homes, some to watch and pray, one to go up. At Canaveral, the evening before the shot, the seven men meet. Six of them surround the seventh, grinning, joking with him, joshing him, teasing. Within themselves, those six men are envious—or they would not be human—but they keep their regrets to themselves. *They* have not been chosen; *he* has. They must wait their turns. Right now their concern is all for him, for this man who has been so close to them for more than three years. He is less than twenty-four hours away from undying glory—or perhaps from a fiery death.

Each of the astronauts has a job to do, as the moment for blastoff approaches. Each one has had a special area of responsibility, and now he concentrates on it, overseeing the engineers who are making the final checks. The man who is to make the shot is isolated, far from the last-minute hectic activity at the base. Perhaps his wife is with him, perhaps he has preferred that she remain as far from Cape Canaveral as possible while the shot is carried out. He may spend some time alone with his chaplain—or he may choose to make his attempt without a religious consultation. Each of the seven is different, each has his own ideas of how those last hours before the shot should be spent.

There is no crowd around him. Admirals and generals are

staying away. Perhaps the NASA chief, James W. Webb, is on hand to have a few words with the astronaut. Possibly the President will phone from Washington to add his encouragement and enthusiasm to the operation.

The astronaut gets a thorough medical check-up as dawn approaches. While the medics are poking and squeezing him, tapping his knees and pressing their cold stethoscopes against him, he gives way to a moment of apprehension. *What if they find something's wrong,* he wonders? *Suppose I have a case of the sniffles, or high blood pressure that developed yesterday, or something like that? Suppose they tell me I can't go, after all, that one of the other guys will have to make the trip this time?*

It would be a whopping anticlimax, he thinks, to have to take a seat on the sidelines after all the handshaking and congratulating of the last few hours. But the medics finish with him, finally. The Flight Surgeon grins at him and says, "Looks like we can stick you in that capsule after all, fella."

"I pass the examination, Doc?"

"You pass," the Flight Surgeon says. "You pass with flying colors, pal."

So there is nothing standing in the way now. It is two hours to launch-time. Out on the field, activity has increased, reaching a feverish pitch as the long countdown enters its last 120 minutes. The fueling crew is busy. Kerosene flows into the tanks, and super-cooled liquid oxygen. Every gauge, every meter, every dial is getting a going-over. By this time, there is no longer any secret about the nature of today's shot. Astronauts are all over the place, their drawn faces revealing tensions they want to pretend they do not feel.

"This is *it*, isn't it?" an engineer asks one of the astronauts. The astronaut shrugs noncommittally without replying. The engineer nods.

"I thought so," he said. "Who's going up?"

The astronaut shrugs again. "Not me," he says with a grin. "You'll read about it in the papers this afternoon."

The countdown continues.

The chosen astronaut and the flight surgeon have entered a van that drives them out to the launching pad. The Atlas

110

gleams with the reflected light of the bright lights flooding the working area. Dawn is still more than an hour away. Heads turn to stare as the astronaut descends from the van, walks across the concrete of the launching pad toward the towering gantry crane that adjoins the rocket.

He feels very alone at this moment.

Step by step, betraying not a flicker of hesitation or doubt, he crosses the launching pad, gets into the elevator of the gantry. He rides to the top, where the capsule sits attached to the Atlas.

"See you around later," he says.

He clambers carefully through the capsule's narrow hatch and lowers himself onto the couch. How many hundreds of times, he wonders, has he settled into this form-fitting couch? In the Johnsville centrifuge, in MASTIF, in the various dummy capsules, in the simulators. He has rested on this same couch during a fifteen-minute ballistic flight through space. But now it's the big one. The orbiting trip.

The countdown is continuing. His earphones bring him the voices of the other six astronauts, as they report in from the blockhouse, nearby, telling him how everything is in order, how each one has checked his phase of the shot to a T. He is glad to hear from them. He feels just a touch of sadness for each of them, because he knows how *he* would have felt in their position. But he shrugs the feeling away. After all, he reasons, he's been chosen because the higher-ups feel he can do the job. This is no time to worry about the left-behinds. The only thing that ought to be on his mind now is the work that has to be done.

"Zero minus fifty minutes," he hears.

He busies himself, checking out the instruments in front of him. They've all been checked before, but he wants to make sure for himself. Outside, technicians and engineers scramble up and down the ladder, bolting his hatch in place, sealing down every connection perfectly.

He leaves his face mask open, not wanting to inflate his bulky and cumbersome pressure suit until it becomes necessary. He is breathing pure oxygen, at a pressure of five pounds per square inch. His environmental system, he notes, is working perfectly. He reports that fact back to the blockhouse, just to be saying something to someone.

111

"Zero minus forty-five minutes."

He continues to check his controls. Through his window, he can see the first pale-pink fringes of dawn starting to streak the gray sky.

"Zero minus thirty minutes."

The fueling trucks are moving away from the launching area. In the blockhouse, men are busily running the final-final checks. Twenty minutes to blastoff, now. Ten minutes. The Atlas stands alone, seeming to strain impatiently at its bonds while the slow minutes tick away.

"Zero minus five minutes."

The astronaut talks to one of his comrades in the block-house. They exchange quips—part of a running gag that they have had going for three years now. The astronaut chuckles. He leans back into the cradling contours of his couch, wishing these final 300 seconds would get themselves over with. He is long since past the stage of nervousness—that happened last night, right after he was told that he was going to be Johnny-on-the-spot come dawn at Cape Canaveral. What he feels now is more impatience than tension. He's already had a fifteen-minute taste of space and come through it okay; now he's due for a couple of hours in orbit, and he's anxious to get up there without sitting around on the launching pad any more.

"Zero minus four minutes."

The astronaut has already run every conceivable check on his controls three times over. There's nothing for him to do now, absolutely nothing for him to do but wait and sit and stare at his panel. So far the countdown has moved along perfectly. *Too* perfectly, he thinks. They were about due for a hitch. One thing he doesn't want now is delay. A "hold" in the countdown might keep him frozen at zero-minus-four-minutes for an hour or two. He itches to be up and away.

"Zero minus three minutes."

Still no snags. Incredible!

"Zero minus two minutes."

He waits, fatalistically sure that something will get fouled up at the final moment. He believes in Murphy's Law, that axiom of engineering that says, *If something can possibly go wrong, it will*. He downright *knows* this countdown will run into a "hold" somewhere in the next 120 seconds.

"Zero minus one minute."

What's happening to Murphy's Law, he asks himself? *Don't tell me they're actually going to get me up on time!*

It looks that way. At zero minus 45 seconds, the connections start to drop away from the booster. Now the count is moving rapidly.

"Have a good trip, spaceman," he hears another astronaut telling him.

"Yeah," he says in return. "Who's buying me that steak tonight?"

Zero minus ten . . .

Nine . . .

Eight . . .

He feels a strange calm now. Ever since 1958 he's sweated and struggled to get himself ready for this moment, and now the moment is actually here. Hard to believe that it's really happening, he thinks. But it is.

Three . . .

Two . . .

One . . .

"Lift off," an astronaut's voice says.

He feels the rumbling of the giant booster engine six dozen feet directly below him. The entire capsule is shaking as the Atlas gathers for the big leap upward. The roar is getting deafening.

He feels no tension. He pities the poor guys in the blockhouse who are watching the launching, who see the Atlas inching off the ground in a pounding fury of smoke and flame and thunder, who are wondering whether it'll make it. He doesn't wonder. He *knows.*

The rocket mounts skyward at a fantastic rate. His control systems are functioning perfectly. Looking out, he can see the Earth starting to shrink behind him. He is up far enough already to be able to make out the hazy shape of the Florida peninsula, specked with low-lying clouds, and then he can see the vast stretch of the eastern coastline of America on the greenish-blue ball below him.

A giant invisible fist presses against his chest, a huge hand flattening him back into his couch. The acceleration is starting to pile up. Four, five, six Gs, the dial says. Eight Gs. He tries to grin, but the effort is a strain. He does a quick mental computation and discovers that his weight is now close to two thousand pounds. Breathing is a struggle. Upward, upward, the rocket's speed getting past 10,000 miles an hour and still gaining.

"How's it going up there?" somebody asks him down at distant Cape Canaveral.

"Fine," he says. "Lots of fun. Just like the centrifuge, that's all it is."

The effort of getting the words out betrays the strain he feels in the grip of acceleration. But he has been through all this before, many times, not only in the centrifuge but in the ballistic flight. He doesn't like life under eight Gs, but he knows it doesn't last long.

The Atlas has just about reached its intended speed of 17,400 miles—five miles a second. It has expended its fuel in a few minutes of fierce and fiery action, and now, burned out, it is separated from the capsule and tumbles away. At the same time, the escape rocket mounted on the nose of the capsule, no longer needed, separates also.

It is a rough moment for the astronaut as his capsule goes its separate way. The retro-rockets mounted on the blunt wall behind him fire, and the capsule lurches away from the Atlas. It goes into a gyrating tumble. But his many hours in MASTIF have prepared the astronaut for this. He holds on, ready to stabilize his capsule manually if one of the many control systems fails.

The control systems do not fail. Automatically, stabilizing jets are fired, and the capsule attains even keel. The needles on the dials in front of him level out. The astronaut smiles. After the 30-rpm torment of MASTIF, the actual separation was a snap!

And now he is in orbit.

To be in orbit means to move in a fixed path about a larger astronomical body. The Moon is in orbit around the Earth. The Earth is in orbit around the Sun. Now the astronaut has his own orbit around the Earth, some 150 miles up. Like all the Sputniks and Explorers and Vanguards that preceded him, he attained orbit by being fired to the right height at the right speed. Now, without the need of any further rocket propulsion, he will—theoretically, at least—keep going on his roughly circular path through the skies, around Earth forever.

Theoretically, that is. Actually, a satellite orbited within a few hundred miles of Earth will repeatedly graze the outlying molecules of the atmosphere, and this atmospheric friction drag will gradually slow the satellite and bring it tumbling back down to Earth. Some satellites, because of the peculiar angles of their orbits, have remained aloft only a few days. Others, less vulnerable to atmospheric drag, will have lifetimes of hundreds of years. But no satellite close to Earth can remain up indefinitely.

This problem is of no concern to the astronaut. Frictional drag will have no chance to interfere with his orbit, because the operation calls for him to remain in space only a few hours. His speed is the same as that of the rocket that delivered him here—17,400 miles an hour. The principle explaining that speed's constancy was set down by Sir Isaac Newton three hundred years earlier—Newton's First Law of Motion, *The speed and direction of motion of every body will remain unchanged unless that body is acted upon by an external force.* Up there in orbit, the only external force that can act to check the speed of the capsule is frictional drag—and its effects are so gradual as to be unnoticeable.

For the first time since his flight began—for the first time, perhaps, since he volunteered for this assignment—the astronaut can completely and totally relax. There is no sensation of motion, no sensation of weight. If there were anything loose in the cabin, it would be drifting in midair, but nothing has been left to drift. The astronaut, who has experienced weightlessness many times, both in his jet training flights and in his ballistic flight, feels the pressure of existence lifting from him. He feels like a disembodied intelligence, an observer without mass or substance looking down on a strange planet.

It is terribly quiet up here. The sound of his own heartbeat is loud in his ears.

Now he can look down at Earth. He is moving faster than any human being has ever moved before—five miles a second—and he can see the geography changing beneath him, though there is no feeling of movement. It is as though he is frozen in the sky, and the universe is moving. There is Hawaii below him now, spread out against the darkness of the Pacific. And he is moving eastward, out of the night, and the United States lies below, cloud-stippled, with tentacles of morning creeping out of the east. Dawn is hours away, here above California, but the capsule continues its steady ride around the world, and there is a lump of awe in the astronaut's throat as he passes from time zone to time zone in a matter of minutes, crossing the mighty Rockies and seeing them only as wrinkled brown ridges in the blue-green ball below, then moving above the cornfields of the Midwest, then into early morning as his capsule passes over the crowded cities of the East.

While he watches, the astronaut talks. He knows there are men clustered down below, eager for any word he'll send back to them. He has routine reports to make—time elapsed since launch, quantity of oxygen remaining, amount of water vapor present in the capsule, the concentration of carbon dioxide in his atmosphere. But he also talks of what he sees.

"There's the coastline now," he says. "The Atlantic is a funny color—purple, almost. I can see the land shading off into the underwater ledge. And now I'm out to sea. Europe is 3000 miles ahead, and I'll be there before you can say Jean Jacques Rouseau."

The cramped quarters, the rigidity of his position, the strangeness of weightless existence—these things don't matter to the astronaut now. His eyes are wide, glowing with excitement. He feels like a small boy on Christmas morning, a small boy who has just been given the whole world as his personal plaything.

London, Paris, Rome, Budapest, Leningrad, Moscow.

All are below him as he moves silently and with incredible speed around the globe. An hour in orbit has passed now, and he has gone two-thirds of the way around the world. He remembers Magellan and his endless voyage, remembers Jules Verne's account of a trip around the world in eighty days. Eighty days! And now, less than a century later, he's doing it in hardly more than eighty *minutes!*

On and on the blunt capsule moves. Tibet is below now. Mount Everest and all the rest of the towering Himalayas pass in review. China. Then over the Pacific again, cutting through the night, on another swing toward the United States.

The viewing port faces down, toward Earth. But by the second orbital trip around, Earth is getting to be old hat to the astronaut.

"I'm going to flip over on my back," he announces. "I'm going to take a look at the big wide universe."

Making use of the manual control skills he acquired during the harrowing hours in the triple cage of MASTIF, he seizes the stick, fires the control jets. The capsule begins to swing over as he tilts it for a look at the heavens. He guides it into position.

Then he gasps as he sees the stars. They gleam like jewels rolled out on black velvet for his inspection. Since there is no atmosphere up here, the stars do not twinkle. Their brightness is blurred by no haze, no city smog, no cloud. There they are, bright hard points of light, a symphony of brightness blazing against the backdrop of space. The astronaut stares until the majesty of it makes him tremble and ache with excitement, and then, reluctantly, he swings the capsule back to face Earth.

"I—I just had a look at the stars," he reports, with a voice choked with emotion. He is annoyed at his own sudden choke-up—but the naked splendor of the heavens has overwhelmed him. "It's—it's—" he fumbles for a few words that will describe what he has just seen. "It's tremendous," he blurts finally, aware that any words he could use would be inadequate. "I don't know how to describe it. You've got to see it for yourselves. That's all there is to it. You've got to come up and take your own look."

The astronaut has nearly completed his second swing around the globe. He has been aloft for three hours, now. He is starting the final orbiting trip. He watches the minutes tick away, and he makes his steady report to Earth, monitoring his instruments all the while. He wonders whether the people on Earth know about him yet. Has the news been broken, or are they saving the story until he returns to Earth? After all, there's still the descent to make. Sitting up here in orbit is a breeze—but coming down can be a little rough.

"Thirty minutes to descent," he calls into his mike. He seals his pressure suit. It inflates quickly and properly, and for the first time since he has gone into orbit he feels a little physical discomfort; the suit is stiff, making it hard for him to maneuver even his fingers. But he has had plenty of practice inside an inflated suit. Those long months of training were anything but wasted time.

Tension is starting to take its toll now. For better than four hours, he has been up here alone in his cramped capsule, thoroughly cut off from the world of his birth. Tough, disciplined man that he is, he still can't help but feel a sense of disorientation, of dislocation. He fights fatigue, which can interfere with his reflexes at the critical time coming. He watches the clock.

"Ten minutes to re-entry."

There is an unexpected pang, now that he is about to leave space. In a strange, dreamlike way he thinks that this is his home up here, that he *belongs* in space, that the descent will be not so much a home-coming as a leave-taking. But he shrugs the weird nostalgia away.

Time for descent now.

The three retro-rockets mounted in the blunt wall behind him burst into life, slamming against the emptiness of space, braking his speed in equal reaction. The braking effect is not great, no more than two or three per cent, but it is enough to deflect the capsule out of its orbit and start it heading down toward the thick belt of atmosphere that surrounds Earth.

The astronaut is alert now, knowing that if his automatic controls fail him at this point he'll be thrown into a life-or-death struggle. He'll need every ounce of skill and luck and ability he has, if that big *if* comes along.

The retro-rockets, having done their final job, drop away. The capsule is coming down blunt end foremost, the astronaut sitting with his back toward the downside. As the capsule loses speed, it descends rapidly. It has traveled some three thousand miles around the Earth since the retro-rockets fired, and it has dropped to a height of only some sixty miles above Earth's surface.

The capsule wobbles and weaves as it hits the first really

concentrated layers of the outer atmosphere. Within the capsule, the temperature begins to climb. The air-conditioning strains to cope with the sudden rise of temperature. Tiny beads of sweat glisten on the astronaut's forehead, even within the cooler atmosphere of his pressure suit.

Outside, a shock wave is forming just ahead of the capsule's blunt nose. The air around the capsule is being heated by the shock wave, heated to a staggering 11,000 degrees Fahrenheit—but the blunt nose pushes most of the heat away to the sides. The astronaut knows the mathematics of it—since the braking force is provided by the atmosphere itself, every bit of the capsule's great kinetic energy is being converted into heat. It works out to 13,500 B.T.U. of heat for each of the capsule's 2000-odd pounds.

Faster and faster, now, the satellite plunges downward through thickening atmosphere. The enveloping layer of heated air is working like a furnace on the outer skin of the capsule. The ablative coating on the blunt heat shield is starting to char, to melt, to strip away into space as vapor. The outer skin of the capsule has reached a heat of several thousand degrees. Inside, the mercury is pushing toward the 115 mark, and the astronaut feels as though he's been thrust suddenly into a Turkish bath.

The deceleration is starting to mount now, too. After four and a half weightless hours, the return of gravity comes with crushing impact, and the G-count rises as the capsule drops. Five, six, seven Gs. And still more.

The capsule has been in the atmosphere only about four minutes now. It seems longer than the entire time spent in orbit. The astronaut manages a grim smile. So far, his automatic controls are handling everything for him. The heat shield is still facing downward, protecting him. The thing that he fears—a wild tumble that will turn the capsule to incandescent cinders—is not materializing.

Now the deceleration is at its maximum. Nine Gs, the astronaut reads. He is flattened against his couch. His heart strains with the effort to push blood through his veins, now that he weighs nearly a ton. The capsule is plummeting practically vertically at this point. He feels his face being distorted like a rubber mask. His eyeballs protest the pressure exerted on them. There is a tightening band of iron around his chest. The heat, the gravitational pull, the uncertainty of his descent—everything seems designed by demons to test a human being to the limits of his endurance. But the astronaut endures. He tells himself that these few minutes of pain and torment are a cheap enough price to pay for the hours of unforgettable wonder up there in orbit.

The capsule is so close to Earth now that its altitude can be measured in feet, not miles. He knows the 20,000-foot level has been passed, because now the snorkel tube is drawing fresh air in from outside, and the temperature in the cabin is dropping rapidly. The capsule is slanting like a blazing meteor through the sky over Florida, its trajectory traced by a thousand anxious eyes at Cape Canaveral.

Any moment now, the atmosphere will be thick enough for the use of parachutes. The astronaut wonders in a kind of detached curiosity whether or not the chutes will work. He's sure they will, but a kind of perverse pessimism comes to pervade him. Everything else has gone so beautifully on this whole trip that *something* has to go wrong. And not much is left to go wrong. He sees that he's coming down right in the impact area of the Atlantic. So, at least, there won't be any bumpy landside landing to worry about.

The braking chute pops open. The capsule bucks and yaws at the sudden interference with its hitherto unchecked plunge. Minutes later, the main chute blossoms out, huge and strong, and the speed of the falling capsule is checked still further. Practically at a snail's crawl now, compared with the dizzy velocities of a few minutes earlier, the capsule drifts toward its rendezvous with the Atlantic Ocean, now less than two miles below.

But even that snail's crawl is a substantial 20 miles an hour, 30 feet a second. The astronaut, no longer crushed by the burden of deceleration's high G- grasp, now prepares himself for the impact of hitting the water.

The capsule cracks into the ocean. A spume of water geysers skyward as a ton of solid metal, still red-hot, plunges into the Atlantic. A bladderlike impact bag beneath the capsule eases the shock, but the arrival is still a nasty jolt. Moments later, the capsule comes bobbing to the surface.

The twenty-minute descent from orbit is over.

All the while, from the moment the retro-rockets were fired, with the capsule high over the west coast of the United States, to the end of the furious plunge in the Atlantic northeast of Puerto Rico, the capsule has been tracked. A tracking station on the Pacific Missile Range had sent a signal to the NASA's Goddard Space Flight Center, near the nation's capital, and computers had worked out the exact impact area. Now rescue ships head for the spot.

Still on his couch, the astronaut lets his breath out in a long, slow sigh.

He's back on Earth.

He knows that it'll be a while before he is picked up. Nothing has been left to chance in the pickup operation. While the recovery ships move as rapidly as they can toward the computed area of impact, search planes circle the vicinity, hoping to spy the tiny capsule drifting in the choppy waves. The capsule is emitting a telltale radio signal for the searchers to home in on. A flashing light stabs at the sky. Aluminum powder is spreading out rapidly on the surface of the water all around the capsule, turning the waves into mirrors that will gleam with reflected sunlight. The capsule has dropped a depth charge that has exploded hundreds of feet down, an explosion that can be detected by sensitive underwater pickups.

But the astronaut does not want to remain in his capsule while the rescue ships plow toward him. He has been confined long enough. Besides, there is an annoying and troublesome sound of splashing water. Is it outside the capsule—or is there a leak?

He decides to board his raft and wait outside the capsule for pickup. Quickly, the astronaut undoes the harness that has held him securely on his couch. He pushes aside the ventilator hose that has been providing cool air for him. Leaning forward, he shoves a section of the instrument panel to one side. Now there is a space just barely big enough for him to crawl through.

He has gone through this exit routine in drills often enough. He moves efficiently, knowing each step well. He pulls open the sealed pressure hatch and slithers through. Now a new wall confronts him: the canister that had held the capsule's braking parachutes.

With nimble fingers the astronaut disconnects the pins that hold the canister in place. He reaches behind him, gets hold of the canvas pack containing his precious life raft and his survival kit. He worms forward again, puts his head down, butts like an angry goat against the canister. His fiberglass helmet with its protective inner lining of leather and foam rubber shields his skull from injury as he batters the chute canister out of the capsule.

The astronaut clambers upward until his head and shoulders protrude from the capsule. The capsule is balanced precariously on its blunt bottom, and as he appears through the narrow end the center of gravity of the capsule shifts, and it tips perilously close to the water. He braces himself and looks around. He is in the middle of nowhere, nothing but water all around, and the high sun of early afternoon is big and bright overhead.

He leans back, tipping the capsule until he is only inches from the water and, slashing open his survival pack, he hauls out the life raft, inflates it, slips it into the water just behind him. A quick scramble and he has wriggled out of the capsule entirely, and onto the raft.

Now he bobs in the sea, a few feet from the capsule. A radio transmitter aboard his raft is sending out a distress signal. He has a mirror for solar signalling, smoke flares, other rescue equipment.

He waits in the choppy sea. He opens his vizor and breathes air again, salty sea air. He fills his lungs with it. He longs to get out of his suit, to take a swim, to wrap himself around a juicy steak. It's been a long day for him, and it isn't over yet.

Half an hour passes, forty minutes, and he begins to wonder if they've all forgotten about him. Then a helicopter whizzes overhead, looking like an angry hornet against the brilliantly blue tropical sky. It hovers, and he waves, and it begins to descend.

A rope ladder dangles.

Then he is on board, and they are pounding his back, and

pumping his hand, and asking him, "How was it? What was it like, huh? How'd you feel up there?"

And this man who has ridden three times around the world in less than three hundred minutes smiles and shrugs and says in a steady voice, "It's pretty grand up there. I can't wait to get a second look."

And he *will* get a second look, and a third, and many more, before his time comes to go to the sidelines and let the new crop of space jockeys take over. But first he has a rendezvous with history, on the mainland. There's a hero's welcome waiting for him—waiting for the first American to orbit through space.

Somehow, the astronaut thinks as he heads landward, he's more apprehensive about that welcome waiting for him than he was about making the flight itself. But he'll just have to grin and bear it, he tells himself. It's the price of fame.

Chapter Eleven

AFTER PROJECT MERCURY

The successful achievement of a manned orbital flight around the Earth is a big and important step in itself. But the culmination of Project Mercury is only the beginning of the conquest of space. It is simply the climax of the first stage of this great adventure.

The National Aeronautics and Space Administration, which is guiding our space program, has already mapped out a detailed and ambitious schedule of the events that will follow Project Mercury. And, we may be sure, our rivals in the Soviet Union have an equally massive space program ready to be unveiled.

~ This is only the beginning.

Once Project Mercury has been carried out, the next name to stud the headlines will be that of Project Apollo, which is ticketed on the timetable for 1965 or 1966—with the hope of earlier accomplishments if a breakthrough in rocket power happens. Project Apollo calls for putting a team of two men into orbit around the earth for an extended period. In order to make Project Apollo a reality, we will have to develop more powerful rockets than we have now. The Atlas, with its top thrust of 360,000 pounds, will be inadequate for lifting more than the very minimal weight of the Mercury capsule.

On the drawing boards and well along in development is the Saturn rocket, which will have vastly more power than any rocket now in the American repertoire. The Saturn will be a three-stage rocket whose first stage, developing 1,500,000 pounds of thrust, will be ready for initial testing late in 1961. The Saturn's second stage will be a cluster of six engines with a total thrust of 90,000 pounds. By 1964, this huge rocket should be capable of lifting manned capsules containing two- and even three-man teams, into outer space.

After the first teams go into orbit, the next step in the American space program will be the Apollo orbiting laboratory—a small "space station" containing a crew of three with supplies to last them several weeks while they make scientific observations in space. The Saturn rocket may not be powerful enough to put an Apollo Laboratory into orbit, but the yet-to-be-developed Nova rocket should serve adequately as the booster. The monstrous Nova will stand 220 feet high—topping the Saturn by 70 feet, and towering 140 feet over today's Atlas missles. Each of its four engines will deliver a million and a half pounds of thrust—and the over-all push should be enough to lift a giant-sized capsule into orbit around the Earth.

In the matter of unmanned space projects, we have a whole cluster of ideas. One that may have been brought into reality before this book sees print is Project Ranger, the plan to land a television camera on the Moon. A Soviet rocket reached the Moon in 1959, but crash-landed, making impossible the sending back of any information. We hope to engineer a "soft" landing that will leave television equipment unharmed. Thus we will get our first detailed close-up views of the Moon's surface.

A weather satellite called Nimbus is in the works for launching late in 1962. Nimbus will be an advanced and far more elaborate version of the Tiros weather-observation satellites, of which several have already been placed in orbit. Further Transit satellites will aid in navigation. A host of complex research laboratories will be orbited, unmanned, in 1962 and 1963, while we prepare for the manned Apollo shots. Planetary probes in the yet-unborn Mariner series will head for Mars and Venus during 1962. By 1964 or 1965, we may be making "soft" landings of equipment on those planets (Project Voyager.)

1966 is the estimated date for the carrying out of Project Prospector—the landing of a mobile, unmanned device on the surface of the Moon. The Prospector, roaming the Moon on tractor-treads, will make important discoveries concerning our first satellite's mineralogical wealth.

The major fly in the ointment, from the viewpoint of the United States, is that the Russians, with their greater rocket power, will always be a step or two ahead of us. As of mid-1961, their biggest rockets were about twice as powerful as ours—a thrust of perhaps 800,000 pounds, as against the 360,000 pounds of Atlas. But, though our Saturn and Nova rockets will eventually leave the 1961 Russian rockets far behind, there is no reason why Soviet scientists cannot keep pace with any of our newer developments—maintaining and even widening today's "booster gap."

Why may they stay ahead of us?

Dr. F. J. Krieger, an Air Force adviser who forecast the Sputnik triumph of 1957, thinks the answer lies in Soviet single-minded concentration, unhampered by red tape or budget requirements. While American space scientists are forced to go through an annual bargaining session with the Congressional appropriations pundits, the Soviets can simply authorize expenditure for research without the need for legislative approval. While our three military services have worked frequently at cross purposes, often actively sabotaging each other's space projects to the greater glory of their own, Russia has a unified space command.

The Soviet stress on fundamental principles and simplicity of design, coupled with streamlining of the chain of command and what Dr. Krieger calls "the happy faculty of making proper executive decisions," results in their widening lead in space research. For the Russians, space is a top-priority operation. The Soviets see in space research their chance to wipe out the world-wide image of American technical superiority.

We, however, with a democracy's traditional slow deliberation of action, have not thrown ourselves into the space race with the same gusto. We have moved along reluctantly at best, goaded by the success reports coming out of Moscow —but the private sector of our economy has taken precedence over public expenditure for research and development, while the quest for a balanced budget is pursued more hotly than the quest for a rocket that can take men to the Moon.

Therefore, we can look forward glumly but realistically to a series of Russian space triumphs a notch or two ahead of our own. We have just launched a man on a ballistic flight, but they have already had one in orbit. While we are still struggling to put up our Apollo teams in orbit around Earth, they will probably be putting similar but bigger capsules in orbit around the Moon. When we are orbiting men around the Moon, they will be making landings there. When we have finally reached the Moon, we will find Russian permanent settlements already established there, taking dead aim on Mars and Venus.

Perhaps not. American scientific accomplishment should never be sold short. The chance of a fuel breakthrough is appreciable, and by 1964 or 1965 we may find that our rockets have caught up to Russia's in thrust, accuracy, and maneuverability. In that case, we will find ourselves in a strenuous neck-and-neck race—with the universe as the prize.

Permanent Space Stations

The great stumbling block in space exploration is the gravitational pull of the Earth. Escaping from this pull is the first job in space exploration.

Newton's inverse-square law of gravitation holds that every particle of matter in the universe attracts every other particle with a force which is directly proportional to the product of the masses of the particles, and inversely proportional to the square of the distance between them. The Earth attracts the particles that make up our bodies. We each, in an infinitesimal way, attract the Earth toward us. The Earth's pull is by far the greater, because its mass is greater than ours.

To escape from this pull, it is necessary to apply a force as great as Earth's gravitational force, in an opposite direction. This force can be calculated fairly easily; an *escape velocity* of 7 miles a second, or 25,000 miles an hour, is needed to break loose from Earth's pull. If the speed of a rocket is 25,000 mph or greater, the rocket will escape from Earth and continue on to infinity, if not checked by a braking rocket or by collision with some astronomical body. If the speed attained is less than 25,000 miles, the rocket will ultimately fall back to Earth.

Space satellites such as the Mercury capsule do not need to attain escape velocity, since they are not intended to proceed on to infinity. All they must reach is *orbital* velocity, a lesser figure, 4.9 miles a second. At this speed they will neither continue on into space nor fall back to Earth, but will remain fixed in a theoretically permanent orbit. Russians call orbital velocity "the first cosmic speed" and escape velocity "the second cosmic speed."

The Russians were the first to attain escape vtlocity in a space experiment, but we have matched that accomplishment by now, having sent a number of our space probes beyond Earth's pull. (Attaining *orbital* velocity is now a relatively simple matter for both nations.)

In order to explore the Moon and the planets of the Solar System, we must build rockets that can attain escape velocity of 25,000 mph as easily as today's rockets reach orbital velocity (approximately 18,000 mph.) In the struggle against gravity, we are designing bigger and bigger rockets, with mightier thrusts that can lift ever-larger payloads. Just as a small boy would struggle to lift a ten-pound weight that a grown man can lift with one hand, so, too, do our present-day rockets strain to their limits to boost one or two-ton payloads that tomorrow's Saturns and Novas will find child's play.

But there is another way out, a way of getting around the knotty problem of escape velocity without having to build ever larger rockets. This is the permanent station in space—and such space stations will undoubetdly be functioning in orbits by 1970 or so.

Space stations will be necessities if space flight is ever to amount to anything. There are certain practical limits on the size of rockets that can take off from Earth. Another of Newton's Laws of Motions—the third—states that, for every change of momentum of a part of a material system, there is an equal and opposite change of momentum for the remainder of the system. This law of equal and opposite reactions explains such phenomena as the recoil of a rifle: as the bullet is propelled forward, the rifle kicks backward with equal but opposite force.

A rocket can be considered as a giant rifle. When an Atlas blasts off, it kicks against the Earth with a thrust of

300,000 pounds. The Newtonian recoil sends the Atlas upward, while the Earth, because it is huge compared with the Atlas, recoils imperceptibly in the opposite direction.

As our rockets get bigger and bigger, the recoil will be more perceptible. A Nova, generating a thrust of some *six million* pounds, will lash out at the Earth with truly mighty force as it rises. But even the Nova's thrust is very small potatoes indeed, considering what kind of power would be needed to lift, say, a spaceship bearing a hundred passengers. We are faced with a situation in which rockets get so big that every blastoff would gouge a giant crater in the Earth. Spaceports would have to be rebuilt after each departure.

The only feasible solution to the problem of increasing recoil is to build a space station which will orbit the Earth and which can be used as the springboard for space flights. The Russians have already made use of this concept in an applied way, when they launched their Venus probe in February, 1961. At that time, they first orbited a heavy satellite, and then used it as a springboard from which they launched the piggyback Venus probe. In this way, it was not necessary for the Venus rocket to attain the escape velocity from Earth, 25,000 miles per second. An orbiting satellite has a velocity of nearly five miles a second. The additional velocity needed to escape from both orbit and Earth is only some two miles a second. Therefore, a much less powerful rocket is needed to reach escape velocity from an already orbiting satellite than from the surface of Earth itself.

Thus the need for a permanent way station in space from which flights could be launched. Of course, the station will have to be fairly large in size, or else it would be thrown off its orbit by the recoils of rockets taking off from it. Putting up such a large station in one piece is obviously an impossibility; if we had rockets that could lift a satellite 200 feet in diameter into orbit, such a station would not be needed in the first place.

But, as our precision control improves, it will be possible to launch such a space station piecemeal. Manned or unmanned rockets containing the raw materials for the station could be placed in orbit—in the *same* orbit—and then assembled in space. Structural units and machinery will drift in complete safety on fixed orbits, while spacemen powered by individual rocket tubes will float around the site, constructing the giant satellite. More construction material can be rocketed up from Earth as the space station takes shape.

The problem that must be overcome before work can start on such a station is one of timing. Since the incomplete satellite, the workmen, and the construction material will all be moving around the Earth at a speed of close to five miles a second, the rockets coming up from Earth must match velocities and orbits exactly. If a rocket supply ship missed its rendezvous by only two seconds, it would go into orbit nearly *ten miles* from the construction site!

Still, the problem of timing is not beyond 1961 technology. And so building a space station will be within our grasp—or the Russians'—as soon as our rockets are powerful enough to assure payloads of big enough size to make the operation feasible. For a probable cost of six to ten billion dollars, a "space wheel" some 200 or 250 feet in diameter could be constructed over a period of seven to ten years. When completed, it would circle the Earth in permanent orbit a thousand or two thousand miles above the surface, and would serve as a base for a military installation as well as a halfway house for rocket flights.

Such a satellite of huge size will have inestimable importance, and beyond a doubt both the United States and the Soviet Union will be constructing space stations that will be operational early in the 1970's.

The military advantages of a space station circling the Earth need not be stressed. Should the Cold War continue on into the space age, such stations, armed with H-Bombs and elaborate electronic scanning equipment, will serve as watchdogs against surprise attacks.

In the event that today's tensions melt within the next decade, the space stations will be available for peaceful uses. Scientific experimentation into weightlessness and low pressure can be carried on easily in such a station. Delicate medical operations which would be impossible under conditions of gravitational pull can be performed under zero-G conditions aboard a space station. Conceivably, in the next century, space stations will become resort areas where the pleasure seekers of tomorrow will go to gambol in weightlessness and peer at the stars.

But, most important, the space stations will make space travel possible. Not only will they serve as refueling stops for rockets being launched from Earth, but they will launch small rockets of their own that can go forth, with only minimal thrust requirements, to explore the Moon and the nearby planets of the Solar System.

The space liners of the next century may never land on Earth at all. Just as today's ocean-going liners anchor well out in the harbor while passengers are ferried to and fro, so, too, the giant space liners will carry their hundreds of passengers from space stations to the Moon or the planets. Small ferry rockets will be used to bring the passengers to and from the orbiting stations. The liners themselves, being too big to be used under Earth's gravitational pull, will have to be constructed in space—and orbiting factories will be constructed first, to build the liners!

By the end of this century, then, the heavens will be studded by dozens of orbiting space stations. Some may have strictly medical uses, others strictly military applications; still others will be factories used for the construction of other space stations or for building space liners. Satellites will be used as astronomical observatories; unhindered by atmospheric distortions, telescope eyes will strike farther into the depths of the universe than is possible today. Meteorologists will be able to study weather patterns on the Earth below and provide weather forecasts of stunning accuracy. Other satellites will be used as telephone and television relay points, making possible global communications at low cost.

Life aboard a space station would be incomparably more comfortable than existence in the cramped confines of a Mercury capsule. The inhabitants will be able to choose their own weight, from zero up, since a space station can create an artificial gravitational pull by spinning on its axis. If a 250-foot space wheel revolved once every 12.3 seconds, centrifugal force would create a gravity pull equal to that on Earth. If it revolved more slowly, the gravity pull would be less strong—$\frac{1}{3}$ G at one revolution per 22 seconds, for instance.

At first, oxygen will have to be shipped up from Earth via supply ships. Later on, plants may be used as oxygen-conserving systems. Water-recovery units will assure a constant water supply. Food will be imported from Earth, at least until the space stations are large enough to develop their own gardens and pastures.

The forerunners of these mighty space stations are already in orbit—the relatively tiny Sputniks and Explorers and such that we and Russia have been launching for the past three years and more. The Mercury flight adds a new factor—man—while the Apollo capsules of a few years hence, with their two- and three-men teams, will be even closer to the desired goal of a space station.

By 1970, the first small permanent stations should be in orbit—certainly the Russians ... nave one up by then, and it is to be hoped th : we will be able to keep pace. These small orbiters will be used as command stations for the construction of the larger "space wheels" that will begin to dot our skies as the decade of the '70s continue.

Reaching The Moon And The Planets

Today's rockets can attain escape velocity, and so can go to the Moon or to the planets; the Russians have already demonstrated this by crashing a Lunik into the Moon and putting other probes in orbit around the Sun, while we have likewise sent space vehicles beyond the grasp of Earth's gravity.

But getting to escape velocity is only the first step. At present, we are unable to guide our probes with anything like real accuracy (only one Moon shot out of perhaps a dozen fired by this country and Russia has come within 5000 miles of target) and we are unable to land them without destroying them. A rocket reaching escape velocity of 25,000 miles an hour maintains that speed until it gets to its destination. Our scientists are working on automatic brake rockets that will slow the Moon rocket to a practical landing speed. (The Mercury capsule used parachutes plus the atmosphere's natural braking effect to slow itself from its 17,400-mph speed. But the airlessness of the Moon makes such steps useless.)

Not only must the Moon rocket carry enough fuel to brake itself, but—when we move on to the manned phase of lunar exploration—it must be able to return to Earth. It will not have the same gravitational pull to overcome on the round trip, since escape velocity from the Moon is only 1.47 miles per second, but the extra fuel must be carried—increasing the weight at blastoff from Earth.

Building of space stations will greatly simplify the fuel problem. A rocket taking off from an orbiting satellite would require a far smaller expenditure of fuel than one blasting off from Earth. Although we will undoubtedly be reaching the Moon directly from Earth long before our space station launching platforms are ready, it will only be after the building of those platforms that there can be any regular and relatively inexpensive travel to and from the Moon.

It will be, of course, impossible for mankind to live unaided and unprotected on the airless, lifeless Moon, with its terrible extremes of temperature. But our experience in creating artificial Earthlike environments aboard orbiting satellites will no doubt help us to carve footholds in Luna. Inflatable plastic domes will serve as shelter, first for teams of two or three men, later for larger groups. Slow expansion over a period of ten or fifteen years will eventually bring us to the point where domed "cities," pressurized and completely sealed, will provide dwelling places for perhaps several hundred people.

Aside from the scientific benefits of reaching the Moon, the practical yield—in terms of raw material and otherwise—is likely to be considerable. The Moon is an untapped world which may prove to be a fertile source of many of the minerals now approaching the exhaustion point here on Earth.

And, too, the Moon will serve as a super-space station in the further conquest of space. Just as the orbiting "wheels" a thousand miles above Earth will be used as the springboards for getting to the Moon, so, too, will the Moon be a jumping-off point for exploration of Mars and Venus.

These are the two planets most likely to be visited during the lifetimes of today's citizens. They are our neighbors in space. Mercury, the innermost planet, is too close to the Sun to permit exploration until the science of refrigeration is far more advanced than it is today. Jupiter, Saturn, Uranus, and Neptune are so far away and so huge that their exploration is still purely in the realm of science fiction, while dark Pluto, three and a half billion miles from Earth, would take decades to reach at today's rocket speeds.

Mars and Venus, though, are within striking distance. Venus comes as close to Earth as twenty-five million miles, Mars fifty million. Both planets are slightly smaller than Earth, so no problems are presented by gravity. (A 200-pound man on the surface of Jupiter would find himself weighing better than 500 pounds, on the other hand.)

So far as we know—and space fantasies to the contrary —Venus and Mars, as well as the other six planets, are not inhabited by intelligent life. There is some reason to believe that Mars has vegetation; we know nothing at all about Venus, whose surface is covered by an impenetrable cloud blanket. But, at least from today's vantage point, it seems safe to say that we will find empty planets, ready for our taking.

Neither Mars nor Venus will be inhabitable by human beings when we get there. So far as we know, the atmosphere of Venus is chiefly formaldehyde, while Mars is all but waterless and has little or no oxygen in its thin atmosphere. Therefore, the early explorers of the planets will need just as much protection as the explorers of the Moon or of empty space itself, while "colonization" of the planets will have to await major scientific accomplishments in the next century.

Already, the Soviets have sent a probe that has passed within a mere hundred thousand miles of Venus. During 1962 and 1963, other probes sent from both sides of the Iron Curtain will approach our sister planets, and probably will reach them no later than 1964.

After that will come the methodical steps—placing of an unmanned satellite in orbit to take observations, followed —perhaps by 1973 or so—by a manned satellite orbiting the planets and returning. We may see manned landings on Mars or Venus by 1975, perhaps even earlier if progress in space station construction makes planetary expeditions more feasible than they are today.

Space travel is not likely to become a civilian pastime before the end of this century. The formidable cost of lifting a rocket will be reduced as mass production enters the picture; new means of propulsion may come along to replace today's rockets, but even so trips will be long in duration and comforts will be few on the space frontier.

The inexorable laws of mass and inertia make space travel an expensive proposition. A certain mass has to be lifted at a certain speed, and today's fuels are just barely adequate for the job. The more fuel a rocket carries, the heavier it becomes, and the resultant vicious cycle is obvious. Therefore, a fixed upper limit on the amount of fuel a rocket can carry exists. Beyond that point, the initial thrust is simply not great enough to lift the overburdened rocket.

Today's rockets expend their fuel in one fierce blaze of glory, burning out in a matter of minutes. A longer period of acceleration at the same exhaust velocity would result in faster rocket speed. Today's rockets, because of their brief acceleration periods before burnout, are inefficient lifters of weight. A solid-fuel rocket with a gross weight of 9000 pounds is carrying some 5700 pounds of fuel to lift a payload of 2000 pounds. It generates a thrust of, say, 32,000 pounds, but burns out after only one minute. With such a rocket, a trip to the moon would last five days.

Other propulsion means besides today's chemical-fuel methods are under development. For instance, a rocket powered by a nuclear reactor would require only 2600 pounds of fuel to propel that same 200-pound payload to the Moon in five days, since the period of thrust would be longer. (In both cases, the trip is not from the Earth to the Moon, but from a space station 400 miles above Earth to a similar one near the Moon.) More advanced space propulsion may be carried out using a beam of ionized particles as the propulsion means; fuel demands would be almost negligible and thrust almost continuous throughout the voyage.

But even if today's propulsion experiments result in important advances, space travel will continue to be a slow business for years to come. Traveling between planets is not like traveling from New York to London. For one thing, the distances are incredibly greater; the Moon, which is the nearest heavenly body, is eight hundred times as far from the Earth as New York is from London—while Venus is a hundred times as far from the Earth as is the Moon! For another, interplanetary travel involves movement between *two moving points*. The trajectory of a ship headed for the Moon must be computed so that the rocket is aimed at where the Moon will be five days from launching, not where it is when the rocket takes off. The science of "astrogation" will thus be complex and difficult.

Trips to Mars and Venus will last more than a year in each direction under favorable circumstances. There are times when Mars and Earth, say, are at extreme ends of their orbits, and the distance between them becomes vastly greater than the average. At such times travel to Mars will be impossible or at least unfeasible.

As for reaching the outer planets, no space scientist of today seriously thinks that it will be done in his lifetime. Quite likely unmanned observation probes will be sent deep into space in the next couple of decades, and by 1980 we may have unmanned satellites orbiting Jupiter and Saturn. Manned flights to those planets will come much later, if at all.

And the stars?

The mathematics are against it. Barring a wholly radical breakthrough in space travel, not even our grandchildren's grandchildren will live in the era of star voyages. The vast distances make any kind of manned trip to the stars impractical. The nearest star, Proxima Centauri, is more than four light years away. (A *light year* is the distance light travels in one year, moving at a speed of some 186,000 miles a second.) It can be seen that a spaceship traveling at the speed of light would take more than four years for a one-way journey to the nearest star. Today's rockets, far from moving at the speed of light, barely attain a speed of *seven* miles a second. At such a velocity, it would take thousands of years to reach even the closest of stars. It would seem that we will explore in our own back yard for some time to come.

The timetable for our unfolding space program has been worked out in some detail, but is always subject to revision. Mankind has a way of picking up gathering speed once a technology is launched. It was only 56 years from the Wright brothers' first rickety flight to the introduction of the Boeing 707 jet liner—but the Boeing 707 is already obsolescent, with talk of 2000-mile-an-hour commercial air transportation by 1970. Similarly, our space program gains momentum from one month to the next, and we may far exceed today's cautious estimates of future progress.

But as it stands today, here is how the United States plans to move into space:

1961-1962——first orbital manned flights around the Earth. Unmanned probes to the Moon.

1963-1964——unmanned probes to Mars and Venus. "Soft" instrument landings on the Moon. Continued unmanned satellite research.

1965-1966——orbital flights around the Earth by multimanned capsule laboratories. Unmanned orbiting of the Moon.

1968——manned orbital flights around the Moon.

1970—manned landing on the Moon. Construction of permanent space stations in orbit around Earth.

Mid-1970's——manned landings on Mars, Venus. Establishment of pioneer settlements on the Moon. Unmanned orbiting probes to the outer planets.

1980——first large-scale exploration and settlement of Mars and Venus by scientific research teams.

Mid-1980's——first manned flights to the moons of Jupiter and Saturn. Beginning of the exploration of the outer planets.

1990——commercial development of space by private enterprise. Health centers on the Moon, resorts on space stations. Interplanetary tourism.

Let's Not Lose The Space Race

The melancholy backdrop to such glowing timetables of future space exploration is the unshakable fact that the Soviet Union is likely to achieve all of this long before we do. They have led in space accomplishments since the dramatic launching of Sputnik, and each of our gains has been followed by an even more impressive Soviet triumph.

The Soviet Union does not have better scientists. Its engineers are no more skilled than ours. Man for man, we can match the Russian rocketry brains. Where, then, do we fall down? Why are we straining so hard just to keep from being left far behind?

One answer is that the Russians are more eager to conquer space than we are. We move as a nation; the Russians are governed by an elite group that need produce only results, not votes. And we—as a nation—are still reluctant to enter the age of space. The Russian ruling elite resolved, perhaps a decade or more ago, to carry the standard of Marxism beyond Earth's borders. We, as a people, have turned our backs on the future, in sharp contrast.

Space research costs money. This is the blunt, undeniable fact that has caused our space-research lag. In Russia, the space program takes priority over all other expense except national defense, and the result is that in Moscow there is a two-year wait for an automobile, a six-month wait for a telephone, but Russia's rocket has hit the Moon.

This country has been reluctant to spend money on space. On April 8, 1961, the New York *Times* quoted Dr. Leon Trilling, Associate Professor of Aeronautics and Astronautics of the Massachusetts Institute of Technology, to the effect that Russia has about sixty space laboratories in operation, each with a staff of 400 scientists and 1,200 to 1,500 technicians. "Soviet space achievements," Dr. Trilling said, "are the result of hard work and of emphasizing that field at the expense of some others."

The very next day, April 9, the same newspaper carried another article headlined, BUDGET MAY CURB 2 SPACE PROJECTS, which told how the requested NASA appropriation of $308,000,000 had been trimmed by the Kennedy Administration to $125,000,000. This represented an 11 per cent increase over the figure budgeted by the Eisenhower Administration, but fell so far short of NASA requirements that drastic cutbacks were announced in the Tiros weather-observation program and in the development of a nuclear-fueled rocket to replace today's chemical-fueled rockets.

This has been the pattern since our space program was born in the days immediately after World War II. During the Truman Administration, outlays for space research were low, and the work that was done was haphazard and badly co-ordinated. The Eisenhower Administration increased the space budget—particularly after the Sputnik humiliation—but no one high in government seemed to have any real awareness of the importance of space exploration, and the extra appropriations were voted more for the sake of maintaining the "national image" than for the genuine desire to explore space.

The fact that it should be necessary to *justify* the space program to the American people is a sobering indication of the fundamental change in the national character during this century. Nobody needed to justify the opening of the New World in the sixteenth and seventeenth centuries. It was there; it offered boundless opportunities; men settled it. Nobody needed to justify the winning of the American West in the eighteenth and nineteenth centuries; it was an inevitable and dramatic expansion.

But now we as a people act as though there are no more frontiers. Every time a new appropriation is voted for space research, well-meaning people write letters to newspapers and to their congressmen to say, in effect, "Why must we spend so much money on rocket ships when there are so many unsolved problems on Earth? Think of all the starvation, unemployment, and human misery that can be aided with the billions of dollars being thrown away on space research!"

Yet this is beside the point. We strive at all times to improve conditions on Earth. Yet we act as though there is simply no way of paying both for rocket ships and unemployment compensation. The man in the street becomes hot under the collar when it is suggested to him that he tighten his belt so much as a single notch for the sake of an increased space exploration appropriation. "Why should I? Why should I give a damn about the Moon?" he is likely to ask.

Despite this attitude, we are, willy-nilly, in a race for space. It has been thrust upon us. The Soviet Union, our bitterest economic rivals, have given notice of their determination to make the universe their own. The choice is simple: we can pull into our shells while the Russians grab the worlds in the heavens—or we can buckle down and try to get out there ourselves.

The Cold War In Space

Obviously, we are trying to get out there. We have not been trying hard enough, evidently, but our lethargy is perishing as each Russian advance drives home the nature of the struggle. The pity of it is that the cold war is being carried into space. What could have been mankind's grandest adventure is becoming a power rivalry.

What is shaping up is the greatest economic struggle since the opening of the New World. We and the Russians will be reaching the Moon and the planets in approximately a dead heat, we hope. By the turn of the century, their bases and ours will have mushroomed on the Moon and perhaps on Mars and Venus as well.

Will we turn all the planets into armed camps? Will we be compelled to divert billions of research dollars into vigilance and security? Will we engage in actual war for possession of the planets?

Or—worse—will Russia reach the Moon, Mars and Venus a year or two ahead of us, plant the red flag, and defy us to land?

There are no laws of outer space. For a decade, international legal minds have cried out for some world-wide convocation that will decide the ground rules for the age of space. Will the first nation to reach a planet have the right to claim exclusive possession? Or will the worlds of space be considered, like the high seas, international territory?

The ideal would be, of course, for all nations, and particularly the United States and Russia, to pool their efforts in space exploration. In his inaugural message, President Kennedy called for such a joint effort. "Let both sides seek to invoke the wonders of science instead of its terrors," he asked. "Together let us explore the stars, conquer the deserts, eradicate disease . . ."

The sentiment is fine, but today, clearly ahead in many phases of space research, the Russians might easily say,

"Why should we join forces with you Americans? We can explore space for ourselves. We don't need your help." And there is no indication that they would ever have been willing to negotiate, even before Sputnik I.

Therefore, today's need is to understand the challenge of space, both as a noble quest for its sake, and as a desperate matter of national survival.

Project Mercury can be a turning point in the Space Age, if we rally and go on from here to further triumphs. We cannot afford to let the Soviet Union freeze us out of space. We are at the crossroads today. If, through superhuman efforts, we catch up with Russia, and even overtake her, the groundwork could conceivably be laid for further space conquest by a joint effort of the peoples of Earth, acting in harmony and concord, rather than by individual clamoring nations bursting with childish pride and striving for propaganda advantage.

THE END

The Epic Story Of The Battle
Of The Bulge—The Greatest
Pitched Battle In America's History

BREAKTHROUGH

By Franklin M. Davis, Jr.

"This battle," Hitler said, "is to decide whether we shall live or die."

Skillfully, secretly, he assembled three German armies—24 divisions, 250,000 men, 970 tanks and 1900 pieces of artillery.

Taking advantage of the harsh winter, he picked a place where the Allied forces were water-thin—four American divisions and one armored cavalry regiment—and unleashed a devastating attack to annihilate the out-numbered defenders.

Thus started the engagement that destroyed forever the myth of the vaunted superiority of the German soldier and proved conclusively the true greatness of American generalship and fighting spirit.

A MONARCH AMERICANA BOOK

Available at all newsstands and bookstores   35¢

The Epic Story Of The Greatest
Airborne Assault Of World War II

ARNHEM

By Major-General R. E. Urquhart

The Allied airborne assault for the control of the lower Rhine had begun. . . . Hundreds of planes spewed out parachutists into the turbulent sky, gliders landed and disgorged jeeps and anti-tank guns. And still no opposition from the Germans. The landing had been a complete surprise.

But two hours later, the orders for the entire operation fell into Nazi hands. Quickly snipers began to appear. SP guns, mortars, tanks and flame-throwers set up a withering curtain of fire.

Allied communications were soon disrupted. Air support failed to arrive and reinforcements were lost in the limbo of chaos as casualties mounted.

And now the real battle began . . . a battle which would decide if these indomitable Allied men of war would fight their way out of this death trap or be annihilated by the enemy.

"A warm and detailed record of one of the great tests of human heart, courage and stamina in the fearful crucible of war."

Miami HERALD

A MONARCH WAR BOOK